School of
HEALTH
&
SOCIAL
WELFARE

K100
Understanding Health and
Social Care

Block 2
People and Places

K100 Production Team

Andrew Northedge (Chair)
Jan Walmsley (Deputy Chair)
Margaret Allott (Course Manager)
Tanya Hames (Course Secretary)
Joanna Bornat
Hilary Brown
Celia Davies
Roger Gomm
Sheila Peace
Martin Robb
Deborah Cooper (VQ Centre)

Jill Alger, Julie Fletcher (Editors); Janis Gilbert (Graphic Artist); Hannah Brunt, Rob Williams (Designers); Paul Smith (Librarian); Deborah Bywater (Project Control Assistant); Ann Carter (Print Buying Controller); Pam Berry (Text Processing Services); Mike Levers (Photographer); Vic Lockwood, Alison Tucker, Kathy Wilson (BBC Producers); Maggie Guillon (Cartoonist)

Regional Education and Training Managers

Lindsay Brigham
Anne Fletcher
Carole Ulanowsky

External Assessor

Professor Lesley Doyal, University of Bristol

This is the K100 core course team. Many other people also contributed to making the course and their names are given in the Introduction and Study Guide.

Designed, edited and typeset by The Open University

Printed and bound in the United Kingdom by Thanet Press Limited, Margate, Kent

ISBN 0 7492 3421 0

For further information on related Open University courses and study packs, write to The Information Officer, School of Health and Social Welfare, The Open University, Walton Hall, Milton Keynes MK7 6AA.

1.1

16992B/k100b2u6i1.1

Contents

Study skills by Andrew Northedge

Introduction

Block 1 was all about the people who give and receive care. We looked in detail at these relationships and how they have been influenced by the family model of informal care and the medical model of health care. The setting or environment in which care took place moved in and out of focus. Sometimes, as at Leeds General Infirmary in Unit 2, or when discussing the intimacies of bathing in Unit 4, we were very conscious of setting, but at other times the setting remained in the background. In contrast, Block 2 is all about places, the environments where care takes place. The aim of this block is to explore the impact of environment on the care received. For a majority of people care takes place in the domestic home, whether it be their own home or someone else's, as in childminding or foster care. But for a smaller group of people, receiving care means a different place to live – a long stay hospital, a residential home, a hostel or spending some time at a day centre or hospital. These 'special' settings have been defined as being for people with 'special needs'. During the course of this block, we hope that you will begin to understand more about 'who lives where' and the way environment impacts upon quality of life.

Unit 6
Places for Care

Prepared for the course team by Sheila Peace

While you are working on Unit 6, you will need:
- Offprints Book
- *The Good Study Guide*
- Audio Cassette 2, side 1

Contents

Introduction

All caring relationships take place somewhere. For a majority of people this place is their own home in the community but this is not always the case. Some people experience care in other people's homes, children being cared for by childminders while their parents work or living with foster families, adults receiving respite care. Many of us experience care in hospital at some point in our lives – a very different environment from our home. A number of adults and children also experience care in what are known as care settings: day nurseries, day centres, day hospitals, hostels, residential care homes, nursing homes.

The variety of places in which people live and the different ways these environments are designed and organised influence how care is given and received and the quality of life. So understanding the impact of different environments on care relationships and care activities and considering accommodation when planning care is important.

The environment can be looked at in a number of different ways, including:

- **the physical environment** – the built environment, its design, the space it occupies
- **the social environment** – the people within an environment, how the environment is used and organised, the roles people occupy within it
- **the psychological environment** – what it means to people and how it makes them feel.

As we go through Block 2 we shall explore these different aspects of environment and the impact they can have on caring. This unit is in four sections: the first three focus on different types of environment for care – the domestic home, 'special needs' housing and hospitals. Section 4 moves our attention to the wider picture of how the households people live in are changing and to the relationship between accommodation and care.

The core questions for this unit are therefore:

Core questions

- Where does care take place?
- How does the physical environment affect the experience of care?
- Why are people who need assistance seen to have 'special needs' and therefore to need 'special accommodation and care'?
- Are places for health care different from those where social care takes place?
- How does the changing nature of families and households affect the relationship between accommodation and care?

We start in the most familiar of environments, the domestic home. This is where most care takes place and where, as we saw in Unit 3, most people feel they have more control over their lives.

Section 1
Home as a place for care

Stop and think about where you live. What's the first thing that springs to mind? Often it's an image of the physical environment (the buildings) that we think of first – a flat within a block, a terraced house, a bungalow. These different physical environments or *forms* of housing could just be called accommodation or shelter, but when we use the term 'home' it immediately conjures up a different set of ideas. These ideas are to do with the social environment – what happens within the building – its *function.* In this section we are going to look at both the *form* and *function* of domestic homes, how the activities which take place in the home are reflected in design, and what this means for home as a place for care. What home means to us will be explored in Unit 7.

1.1   Ideas about home

What ideas do we connect with home? These pictures have probably already triggered some thoughts.

Activity 1   **Ideas about home**

Allow about 10 minutes   Here are some familiar traditional sayings about home. They come from British culture and they conjure up certain images.

> *Be it ever so humble there's no place like home.*
>
> *Home is where the heart is.*
>
> *Home sweet home.*

A woman's place is in the home.

An Englishman's home is his castle.

The man of the house.

How would you sum up what the first three sayings are trying to express?

What do the last three sayings tell us about the relationship between men and women with regard to the home and its function?

Comment   There is a sense here that home is very highly valued whatever its size or status. It is the place where intimate relationships between people are played out – 'where the heart is'. Home is also seen as a place of the family, whereas a hotel or a hostel could accommodate people who are unrelated and in some ways less intimate than family members. There is also a sense of permanency about home. It's where you 'belong'.

Home has also been seen as a place where women's domestic work takes place. The nurturing of children and the care of family members all go on within the home and domestic activities – cooking, washing, bathing, cleaning – are all a part of the traditional work of the housewife.

While women may exert quite a lot of control in the home, over its day-to-day management, in British society men have commonly exercised authority, especially over ownership of property.

So ideas about home have traditionally been very tied up with ideas about the roles of men and women. They are culturally defined and often based on broad stereotypes about who does what (Davidoff *et al.*, 1976). In other cultures and at other times these roles may be thought of in different ways, for example think back to Unit 1 and the way Nelson Mandela talked about the different Kraals or homesteads occupied by his father's four wives.

1.2   The public and the private

So the home is seen as a centre of family life, housework and family care. But this may not be its only function. In the pre-industrial and early industrial periods the home was often the focus of family employment (see Stevi Jackson's comments in Unit 1, Section 5.2). Paid home-working has often been a part of home life, especially for working class people. Women, in particular, have combined housework and carework with paid employment done from home. (I am typing this unit sitting in my bedroom.) And now men are increasingly working from home.

Yet while some paid work has always taken place within the home, during the earlier part of this century the role of housewife as the dominant occupation, particularly for middle-class women, was established as an ideal. A distinction was established between what has been called the *private sphere* of the home and the *public sphere* of paid employment (Garmarnikow *et al.*, 1983). The view emerged that 'real work' in the shape of paid employment, took place somewhere other than the home, and as a consequence housework and carework were invisible, unpaid and acquired a devalued status. The home came to be associated with *reproduction* (having and caring for children), *consumption* (the buying of goods to serve the family) and centred more and more on the nuclear family of one or two generations. Nuclear and extended families were discussed in Unit 1, Section 5, and you might like to look back at this. Notice also, the way public and private has been used here and compare with the definitions given in Unit 3.

1.3 Housework, carework

Housework and carework are major activities which take place in the home. You began to consider the relationship between the two in Unit 3 when you looked at home care. Home care, as a service, has moved away from housework towards offering more personal care but traditionally both areas of work have been the province of the 'housewife'. Activity 2 looks at these areas of work in more detail.

Activity 2   Housework, carework

Allow about 15 minutes   Take a sheet of paper and make two columns headed *housework* and *carework*. List all the activities you would put under these different headings. Now think about the roles of informal and formal carers within the home environment, go through your list and consider who might do each of these tasks. Make some notes.

Comment

Housework	Carework
Cleaning	Washing/bathing people
Washing clothes	Feeding
Cooking	Taking to the toilet
Shopping	Giving medication
	Dressing

No doubt you will have come up with similar lists. Although an informal carer might do all these tasks, they would usually be done by a variety of different formal carers, and a distinction could be made between caring for the person and caring for the environment. A home help or a private cleaner may concentrate on cleaning and perhaps doing some shopping, whereas a home carer or personal assistant comes to assist with the 'personal services' of an individual who needs care and a nurse will come in to give medication.

Areas such as cooking and washing clothes can be met by meals-on-wheels and a laundry service. In special care settings, like a residential care home, this separation between caring for the person and caring for the environment is reflected in the roles of care assistants and domestic staff, although sometimes their roles become blurred.

The separation of different activities within settings has been reinforced through building design; how space is organised has implications for carework and housework.

1.4 Housing design and caring

The age and type of accommodation we live in today varies enormously and the form which domestic housing takes has evolved over time. Housing type and design reflects a range of factors not least the financial resources available to build, the intervention of the state in housing development, and understandings of family life among architects, planners and builders, who have been and remain predominantly male.

Consequently many people may live in ordinary housing which does not always meet the needs of those involved in giving or receiving care.

Activity 3   **House design**

Allow about 40 minutes

In 1984, a group of women involved in architecture and design who formed a group known as Matrix, set out to reconsider the thinking which had underpinned the design of urban housing in Britain from a woman's perspective. Turn now to the Offprints Book and read Offprint 9.

As you read, think about the following questions and make some notes:

(a)   What ideas do the authors suggest lie behind the design of family housing? Have they changed over time?

(b)   What effect might the design of one of the houses discussed here have on caring for someone with a long-term illness at home today?

Comment   (a)   In terms of ideas, I thought of the following:

- the housing discussed in the article is dominated by 'family housing' seen as a nuclear family with two adults and two children. This is very different from the early form of housing which housed a wider range of family and non-related members and also incorporated a 'workplace'
- women are seen as servicing the family
- privacy is seen as important to family life but as the article points out little privacy may be provided for individuals within the family
- the changing design of housing has been associated with improving health through sanitation, ventilation, use of space
- during the past 20–30 years there has been greater recognition of the needs of children within house design.

(b)   When I thought about caring for someone with a long-term illness at home, I focused on the plan for the terraced house and I thought about ways in which they could be provided with some 'peace and quiet' while at the same time keep warm, and not be too far from the WC or the kitchen. A common answer is to bring the bed downstairs into the living room or front room which many older people do today. But of course this does mean a loss of privacy. You may find that the

Bed-sitting room?

bedroom becomes the room you enter into from the street. Today moving the bed downstairs may enable someone to live all on one level but there may be a need to arrange for a downstairs toilet or use of a commode.

The Matrix study was published in 1984. It does not cover the types of housing developments seen earlier in this century in cities such as Glasgow, Edinburgh or Belfast, but it does offer some more general ideas about housing development and the type of housing many people live in today. However, it also focuses specifically on women's roles in the home from the perspective of the dominant cultural majority in the UK. It does not consider the implications of these designs for people from minority ethnic, religious and cultural groups who may have different needs in relation to sleeping and eating spaces, washing, cooking or storing food, for example (National Federation of Housing Associations, 1993).

A number of changes have also taken place in housing provision since the article was written, notably a decline in house construction overall, but particularly of planned council housing. In contrast, private development of housing for sale has increased as have developments by housing associations. Within this new housing there has been an increase in accommodation for one or two persons. However, in general, housing in the 1990s is built to much smaller space specifications than 20–30 years ago since the de-regulation of space standards. The way homes are designed can make a significant difference to the experience of care at home.

Key points

- There are a number of different ways in which we can consider our environment including physical, social and psychological perspectives.

- For many people home is the most familiar place they know and where most care takes place.

- The home has traditionally been seen as a 'woman's place'.

- Home is also seen as a private place and a centre of domestic work and carework.

- Dominant ideas about family life which have been important at different times in history have been incorporated into the design of family housing.

Section 2
Disabling environments

2.1 Environmental stress

Of course, much of the housing described in the Matrix article is still in use today. And many people may find that their actions are constrained by environments which do not meet their needs. Having children can be a time when people begin to realise that the housing they have lived in and coped with quite adequately now presents physical problems.

> *Our hall is particularly narrow, so I knew a normal pram was out of the question and I bought one of those pram-buggies, and when Kim was very tiny he spent most evenings with us in the kitchen while we cooked and ate and we'd have the pram set up and take it in turns rocking it with one foot so we'd have some peace and quiet while we ate. When I wanted to go out I would have to (1) take the bouncing chair down to the hall, (2) come upstairs to the kitchen (two flights) and dress Kim in his outdoor clothes and take him down and strap him in the chair, (3) go upstairs and carry the carry-cot and blankets down to the hall (very difficult to manoeuvre this quite heavy object down the narrow stairs), (4) take the buggy wheels down the steep front steps to the pavement and set them up, (5) take the carry-cot down to the pavement and fix it to the wheels, shouting through the open front door to Kim so he didn't feel abandoned, (6) rush in and get Kim (hoping no one was wheeling the pram away) and carry him down the front steps and put him in the pram and at last set out on our expedition.*
>
> (Foo, 1984, p. 123)

And while women spend a great deal of their time in the home carrying out domestic tasks many find that the kitchen design is far from ideal.

> *You can tell it was a man who designed council houses. A woman can see lots of faults in the design of them. They should have had a woman around to put her spoke in at the time. For instance when they design new council houses they should make much bigger kitchens and put more electric points in and have them higher up the wall to save bending all the time.*
>
> (Rooney et al., 1989)

Within the majority of our housing there has been no recognition at all that some people might have special design needs due to particular handicapping conditions. Designing for the so-called ordinary family is seen as totally separate from designing for people who may be experiencing problems with mobility, agility, sight, hearing – they are seen to have 'special needs', although they may just be experiencing part of the normal process of ageing.

Yet, as the following comments show, adapting properties can produce less than satisfactory results.

> *I live in Boothtown in two terraced houses that have been knocked into one. Because I have Spina Bifida I have special design requirements. There is a ramp up to the front door, wider doorways and an adapted bathroom. The house has its limitations and I have difficulties. I have to*

go in forwards and reverse to come out of the bathroom, and can only just squeeze into the kitchen. It doesn't make it easier when grant applications and planning permission get turned down. My list of design essentials for a new house would include a wide bathroom, with moulded seating in the bath and easily operated pulley, a wide kitchen and generally enough room for me to turn round in my chair without difficulty.

(Rooney et al., 1989)

As this comment shows, some ordinary housing is almost too problematic. Where a person has a physical disability which leads them to use a wheelchair, living in ordinary housing can present many problems. The environment can become a barrier to everyday living – it is a disabling rather than enabling environment.

Disability Discrimination Act 1995

The Disability Discrimination Act 1995 partly came into effect in December 1996 when it became unlawful to refuse to provide services, or provide services of a lower standard, or on a less favourable basis to disabled people on the basis of their disabilities. There are many ways the Act could be used to challenge policies and practices. One important area is accessibility to buildings and transport. However, these provisions are to be phased in over a period of time and may not come into force for nine years which has angered disabled people's groups. Making services accessible will be costly and no additional funding has accompanied this legislation.

2.2 Esther's story

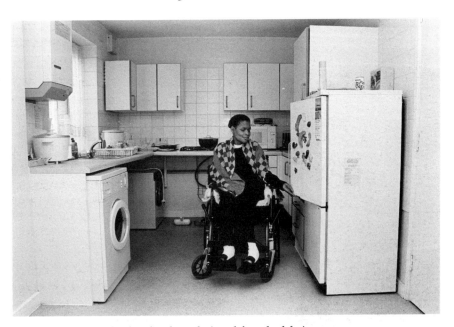

Esther at home; the kitchen has been designed for wheelchair access

Activity 4   Home from hospital

Allow about 30 minutes

Listen now to Esther Hurdle's story on Audio Cassette 2, side 1, stopping at the end of the first section. Esther is 37 years old and lives in Leytonstone in East London. She has multiple sclerosis which has developed gradually over the past 17 years. She now uses a wheelchair. As you listen, think about:

(a)   how the physical environment became a barrier to Esther living her own life

(b)   how the physical environment of her new home has enabled her to take more control over her life

(c)   the needs that she still has

(d)   the extent to which the changes in Esther's physical environment have affected her family.

Make some notes on each of these topics. You may wish to play this section through more than once.

Comment   What are some of the things you noted?

(a)   Esther was in hospital for three years and towards the end of her stay, she was really just stuck in a rehabilitation unit waiting for the availability of housing where she could use her wheelchair and do things for herself and her family. She could only visit her family at weekends because they lived in a third floor flat which wasn't suitable for a wheelchair user and had problems of access. An inadequate lift meant that her husband and sons had to carry her up and down stairs.

Esther felt very frustrated by this situation and in conversations with her, she commented on a sense of powerlessness and helplessness at a time when she was coming to terms with her condition and using a wheelchair. Her daughter was three years old when she first went into hospital. She very much wanted to be a mother to her daughter but instead people had to do things for her. The physical environment had become a barrier to her. While their flat had accommodated the family it could not accommodate the needs of a disabled mother.

She waited and waited. At first the local authority sought to adapt the family's flat or find alternative local authority accommodation but eventually her social worker suggested they go on the waiting list for a housing association that was developing housing which contained four mobility/wheelchair housing units.

(b)   The design of the new house enabled her to be discharged from hospital. It was designed for someone who uses a wheelchair and is spacious with a lift that enables access to the upper floor, doors that are wide and surfaces that can be reached. Esther can now do some of her own self-care such as going to the toilet and other daily tasks such as getting herself something to eat. She is also able to move around and sit in the garden.

(c)   At the moment one of the things Esther can't do for herself is have a bath. The accommodation was not tailor-made to Esther's needs and so she is waiting for an adaptation to the shower. This is one of the remaining areas within the house that needs to be considered and will obviously give her further control over her own life.

While life within her home has improved enormously the external environment still puts up barriers and creates needs. Having access to the resource of an electric wheelchair would obviously make a big

The lift enables Esther to make full use of the house

difference to Esther's mobility – but even with such a chair many areas of life remain 'a disaster'. Esther's comments on shopping reveal the limitations to life that wheelchair users experience through the barriers which our environment throws up every day, from broken pavements to inaccessible shops.

(d)   Did you notice that the new house had met the needs of other members of the family as well as Esther's? She comments:

They're quite pleased with it, especially my little girl, she's quite happy cos she's got a garden to play in and she's quite happy but in the flat she was more fed up cos she wasn't allowed to go out to play on her own but now she's got freedom, just like I've got freedom.

While Esther's comments focus mainly on the way in which the physical environment enables her to be more in control of her own life, they also show Esther to be very much a part of her family. She is now more able to take on the responsibilities of being a carer herself, particularly for her youngest daughter, a role she really missed.

The second part of Esther's story is used in Unit 7, so do not rewind the tape.

Specialised housing

Wheelchair housing is housing generally designed or converted to official standards for people confined to or totally dependent on wheelchairs.

Mobility housing/housing adapted for disabled people covers accommodation built to official mobility standards for people who can walk but with difficulty. It also includes all accommodation that has been adapted specifically for use by disabled people.

Figures for 1993 showed that there were 89,802 units of subsidised specialised housing for disabled people in England (69 per cent mobility housing and 31 per cent wheelchair housing). However, there are wide variations between different regions.

(McCafferty, 1994)

2.3 Home for life

The issue of designing specifically for people with 'special needs' calls into question why 'ordinary' housing cannot accommodate the needs of people with particular physical and mental disabilities. As we heard on the audio cassette, Esther and her family originally had difficulty with a lift and three flights of stairs as well as all the other aspects of their flat which meant that Esther had to rely on someone for every little thing. So what issues would your home environment reveal?

Activity 5   **Design for living**

Allow about 15 minutes   In this activity, think about where you live and make a list of all the things you would have to change to make your environment more accessible to someone with a disability. To help you do this you might like to think about someone you know who has a disability, or a young person who is blind, or an older person who uses a walking frame and is also very deaf. If you are a person with a disability, or live with someone who is disabled, then you may have already tackled some of these issues. You might also like to reflect on aspects of your environment which you would like to change to make your own life more bearable.

Comment

I can't tell what you came up with, but here are some of the thoughts I had about my own home which is a garden flat within a semi-detached house (built in 1908). First of all there are steps both from the street to the front path and then from the front path to the house, so a ramp would be needed for a person using a wheelchair to gain access. The entry buzzer is rather antiquated. It's at a low height but not very clearly marked, and if you couldn't see it would be useless because it's flat and not very tactile. Also it is difficult to hear the buzzer in some parts of the flat – once again, little use if you can't hear it. The front door is very wide but from the hall there are doors and stairs to several flats and they are all too narrow for a wheelchair. In fact the way the house has been converted into flats means that all corridors are very narrow. Changes would be out of the question without a major conversion and the cost of that – well, no doubt it would be prohibitive.

There are some pluses though. The layout is very simple, everything is on one floor and all the rooms lead from one central corridor. So if I had problems orienting myself, or could not see very well I might find this helpful. I do not have to climb stairs once I am in the flat. However, the living room is at the front of the house and the kitchen/dining room is right at the back separated by a corridor. So it's very difficult to make yourself heard from one part to another. I realise now that a lot of shouting goes on because of this layout. There is a phone at either end though, so I suppose these could be used more productively if someone could not hear well.

The toilet and bathroom are on the same floor, but they are all in one. This means that space for turning around is limited. Certainly you could not get into it in a wheelchair. In the kitchen the sink is boxed in and the shelves extend to the ceiling, again none of this is very helpful to those with mobility problems. At present if we need something on a top shelf we have to stand on a stool.

Ideal homes? Windows can be difficult to open

One of our course testers made these comments about her home.

> *I live in an ex-LA house (end of terrace) built in 1930. There is a step up to the front door and to the back door, and a narrow side passage. It would be impossible for a wheelchair user to access. The bathroom is downstairs but very small – just room for the bathroom suite. We removed the basin and exchanged it for a 'cloakroom vanity basin' to give more room. Stairs steep and narrow – doorways not very wide. Sound does not travel well between rooms (e.g. cannot hear phone – situated in hall from kitchen). Would be a nightmare to adapt. (P.s. we love it!!)*

While another reader added:

> *I always think the issue of taps is a good one. It would be just as easy to have those taps like surgeons use that you just press to the side rather than turn on. In fact easier for everyone, particularly when you've got floury hands, but ...*

All these comments begin to reveal some of the physical limitations of the environments we live in. Some solutions would be beneficial to us all. At the same time, many of us who do not have to cope with a disability fail to see the limitations until we are faced with them, for example when an older relative comes to stay. Instead, as the comment above exemplifies, we become very attached to our homes and their idiosyncrasies.

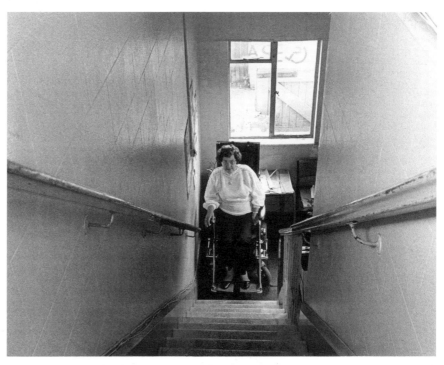

A disabling environment

What this simple exercise shows is that where the environment puts up barriers, there are limited options to:

- try to adapt what there is
- try to move to something more suitable (that is if (a) it can be afforded, (b) somewhere more suitable can be found – often not very easy), or
- rely on other people to help.

Accommodation and care are intimately entwined and in some cases it is the failure to meet accommodation needs which leads some people to leave their homes and move into a more specialised care environment.

While the design of the environment may put up barriers, so too may the maintenance of our accommodation. For many older people basic maintenance in terms of painting and decoration may be an issue, as well as concerns over heating and insulation, or keeping the garden in respectable order. In some areas Care and Repair or Staying Put schemes have been developed, but in contrast to the amounts of money spent on sheltered housing schemes and residential care homes for older people, the amounts of money spent on enabling people to maintain and adapt their physical environment appear comparatively small.

Staying Put and Care and Repair schemes

Home improvement agencies first developed in the voluntary sector in the late 1970s. Today, the government through the Department of the Environment funds 50 per cent of the running costs of approved staying put schemes. Some of these schemes come under the umbrella of Care and Repair Ltd, a national co-ordinating body which promotes good practice and advises government. Others, like the 44 schemes falling within the Anchor Staying Put project, find additional finance from charitable organisations and trusts such as Rowntree, Sainsbury's and the Anchor Housing Trust. The schemes were created to help older owner occupiers remain in their own homes and they offer help and advice over financing improvements and obtaining grants, as well as the actual work of repairs, adaptations and improvement.

(Randell, 1995)

The discussion so far has shown that our domestic housing has been built for those who:

- do not have trouble climbing stairs or are not responsible for carrying others up them
- do not need to use a wheelchair
- can see and hear perfectly well
- are always able to bend and stretch, and
- never, never have difficulty ...

Do you know any of these people? (Yes, but it's not everybody.) The argument here is that the environment which is so disabling to people who do have particularly handicapping conditions is also disabling to everyone – it's just that most people are able to get by. This is one of the reasons why money is spent more readily on 'special needs' housing where accommodation and care are commonly linked together and targeted at people with particular disabilities. But is this labelling as 'special needs' disabling in itself? Is it a coincidence that the very people who have to put up with these environments, and who are often informal carers as well as people who need care, are some of the most disempowered people in our society?

2.4 'Special needs' housing

Activity 6   **So why complain about 'special needs' housing?**

Allow about 20 minutes   Read Offprint 10, 'Fundamental principles of non-discriminatory housing'
    from *Demolishing 'Special Needs'* published by the British Council of
Organisations of Disabled People, in which they set out their case for
doing away with the whole idea of the concept of special needs. Some of
the arguments about the medical model and independent living have
already been explored in Units 2 and 3 of Block 1. (Check back to Unit 2 if
you need to remind yourself about the medical model.) Here we are
concerned with the impact of these views on people's living environments.
As you read try to answer the following questions:

(a)   What are the consequences of the medical model for the services
provided for disabled people?

(b)   What does the social model of disability propose?

(c)   What is the outcome of a 'special needs' approach to housing?

(d)   What do disabled people want?

(e)   What is the impact of Independent Living on the relationship between
accommodation and care?

Comment   The article highlights the following.

(a)   The traditional 'medical model' of disability sees disability as 'located
in the individual, their medical condition and resulting functional
limitation'.

(b)   The 'social model' of disability sees the 'problem' lying with the
'environmental and attitudinal barriers within society itself' rather than
the functional limitation or impairment of the individual.

(c)   Independence is equated with not requiring assistance and services.
For those who do 'require assistance' accommodation is generally
segregated and 'comes in "special" forms'. This has led to
accommodation and care for people with disabilities to be equated
with 'special needs' housing.

Separate funding has been established for 'special needs' housing,
and it has become an industry using up vast amounts of resources.

(d)   Disabled people want 'affordable, accessible housing, with personal
assistance and full access to the opportunities available in society
which most non-disabled people take for granted'.

(e)   Independent Living does not see personal assistance as tied to
buildings. However, the authors argue that some professionals see
'special' housing schemes as offering independent living.

This view confronts the tendency to develop care environments for
groups of people but it does not solve the issues raised by housing
which is unsuitable and needs adaptation. Resourcing imaginative
adaptation of ordinary housing alongside personal assistance is the
answer for some disabled people. Another way of demolishing 'special
needs' is to take a new look at house building and to begin to develop
homes which can be adapted across the life course. The Joseph
Rowntree Foundation have developed criteria for what they call
Lifetime Homes. These criteria are given opposite and, as you will see,
incorporate ideas around accessibility and adaptability.

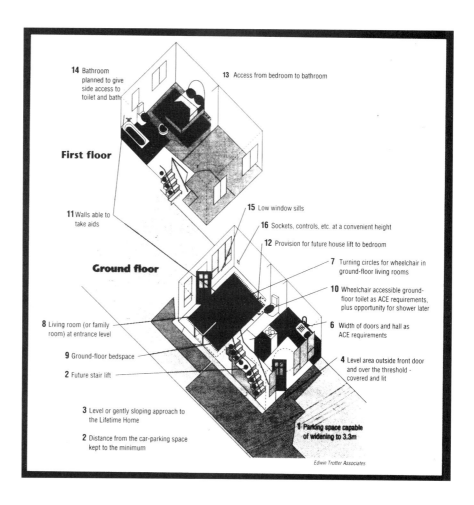

Edwin Trotter Associates

First floor

14 Bathroom planned to give side access to toilet and bath

13 Access from bedroom to bathroom

11 Walls able to take aids

15 Low window sills

16 Sockets, controls, etc. at a convenient height

12 Provision for future house lift to bedroom

Ground floor

7 Turning circles for wheelchair in ground-floor living rooms

10 Wheelchair accessible ground-floor toilet as ACE requirements, plus opportunity for shower later

8 Living room (or family room) at entrance level

6 Width of doors and hall as ACE requirements

9 Ground-floor bedspace

4 Level area outside front door and over the threshold - covered and lit

2 Future stair lift

3 Level or gently sloping approach to the Lifetime Home

2 Distance from the car-parking space kept to the minimum

1 Parking space capable of widening to 3.3m

A Lifetime Home incorporates all the relevant standards listed below.

Access

1 Where car-parking is adjacent to the home, it should be capable of enlargement to attain 3.3metres width.*

2 The distance from the car-parking space to the home should be kept to a minimum and should be level or gently sloping.*

3 The approach to all entrances should be level or gently sloping.* (Gradients for paths should be the same as for public buildings in the Building Regulations.)

4 All entrances should be illuminated*** and have level access over the threshold,* and the main entrance should be covered.

5 Where homes are reached by a lift, it should be wheelchair accessible.*

Inside the home

6 The width of the doorways and hallways should accord with the Access Committee for England's standards.*

7 There should be space for the turning of wheelchairs in kitchens, dining areas and sitting rooms and adequate circulation space for wheelchair users elsewhere.***

8 The sitting room (or family room) should be at entrance level.*

9 In houses of two or more storeys, there should be space on the ground floor that could be used as a convenient bed space.

10 There should be a downstairs toilet** which should be wheelchair accessible, with drainage and service provision enabling a shower to be fitted at any time.

11 Walls in bathrooms and toilets should be capable of taking adaptations such as handrails.

12 The design should incorporate provision for a future stairlift* and a suitably identified space for potential installation of a house lift (through-the-floor lift) from the ground to the first floor, for example to a bedroom next to the bathroom.***

13 The bath/bedroom ceiling should be strong enough, or capable of being made strong enough, to support a hoist at a later date.*** Within the bath/bedroom wall provision should be made for a future floor to ceiling door, to connect the two rooms by a hoist.

14 The bathroom layout should be designed to incorporate ease of access, probably from a side approach, to the bath and WC. The wash basins should also be accessible.***

Fixtures and fittings

15 Living room window glazing should begin at 800mm or lower, and windows should be easy to open/operate.***

16 Switches, sockets and service controls should be at a height usable by all (i.e. between 600mm and 1200mm from the floor).***

Notes

* Designated as 'essential' in the Housing Corporation Scheme Development Standards.

** Designated as 'essential' in the Housing Corporation Scheme Development Standards for five persons and above dwellings, and recommended in others.

*** Designated as 'recommended' in the Housing Corporation Scheme Development Standards.

A Lifetime Home (Joseph Rowntree Foundation)

Housing and independent living

The discussion of independent living in Unit 3 and the Reader chapter by Morris highlight the importance of accessible housing alongside personal assistance if disabled people are to gain control of their lives.

It is therefore very important that housing need is not neglected when people's health and social care needs are assessed because finding ways to enable people to continue to do, or begin to do, things for themselves opens up choices. In a recent study of housing choices and community care researchers pointed to three important areas of policy:

> First, most people in need of community care services are assumed to be already living in their own homes and wishing to stay there. Secondly, while community care needs may be formally recognised, entitlement to housing is limited to a small proportion of those in receipt of community care services. And thirdly, housing requirements are expected to be recognised and dealt with as part of the 'needs assessment' process set up by social services authorities under the system of care management.

> (Hudson et al., 1996)

In terms of assessment, liaison between professionals in housing, social services and health services is particularly important. This is an area where the expertise of occupational therapists (OTs) can prove particularly useful. Many OTs who are now care managers already offer advice to colleagues over assessment, and further information on ways of assisting people to move towards independent living can be gained from Centres for Independent Living which are run by disabled people themselves.

Independent Living Centres

These have been set up by professional service providers (usually occupational therapists) and originally were demonstration centres for aids and equipment. In the first instance, they were aimed at providing information and demonstrations to professional workers, although many now provide direct advice to disabled people.

Centres for Independent Living or Centres for Integrated Living

These were originally started in the USA and are entirely staffed and managed by disabled people. They provide direct services such as counselling, advice on benefits as well as help with employing personal assistants and other workers. There is a national co-ordinating committee set up by the British Council of Disabled People.

As we heard from Esther Hurdle, the role of professionals can be crucial in helping to facilitate a move – for her the social worker's contact with the Housing Association eventually got things moving after a long delay. In their study, Hudson and her colleagues interviewed a number of people with a range of mental and physical health needs, who were either interested in moving to a more independent living situation, or had recently moved. Their experience highlighted the following obstacles to moving:

- *fears of (and subsequent adjustment to) a major change of environment and living circumstances*
- *poor planning and communication*
- *lack of suitable housing*
- *inadequate support to make the move*
- *financial constraints*

as well as these positive influences:

- *a committed professional*
- *personal initiatives by the individual*
- *established organisational pathways into housing.*

(Hudson et al., 1996)

Whether moving to independent living, adapting current housing or moving to a more supportive environment, housing and care go hand in hand, and we return to issues raised here in both Units 7 and 8.

Key points

- Ordinary housing often presents design problems for people caring for children and adults.
- Sometimes these problems can be solved by adapting the environment or moving house. Some people do not have these options.
- Ordinary housing often presents physical barriers for disabled people.
- Some older people and disabled people have to move to 'special' care settings because of the physical barriers they experience in their own homes.
- Some disabled people have to remain in 'special' care settings, including hospitals, because there is a lack of suitable housing.
- Housing needs must be considered alongside care needs.

Section 3
Hospital as a place for care

3.1 Places for health care

The one environment where many people experience care which is least like the domestic home is the hospital. Yet as we saw in Unit 2, a great deal of what we call 'keeping ourselves healthy' takes place in and around the home. Here we pick up on some of the issues about health care from Unit 2, but with the focus on the physical environment.

Activity 7   **Places for health care**

Allow about 5 minutes   Think for a moment about where your health care needs (both physical and mental) are met. Make a list of all the places where you have experienced health care. Now think about other people. Would their experiences add other places to your list?

Comment   One of our course testers produced this list:

- At home – all minor ailments cared for at home. I also have diabetes and I manage this from home or work or wherever I happen to be.

- GPs part of group practice at a Health Care Centre.

- Local general hospital – I attend the diabetic clinic every six months. I also attend the hospital chiropodist on a regular basis.

- I had both my children in hospital and was born in one myself.

- I have been an inpatient on an acute medical ward twice, once as a child.

- I have consulted a homeopath at a different type of health centre – more like someone's house.

In the main most people deal with their health needs at home often with medicine bought over the counter or tried and trusted remedies. Many people go to their local GP if they are feeling unwell but some people will also consult practitioners who offer alternative medicine – homeopathy, acupuncture, herbal medicine for example. Some surgeries are still based in domestic housing but it is more common for GPs to group together in health centres. In a medical emergency a GP might be called out to the home, but many people would think twice before doing so, and depending on the problem decide when it might be better to go to the accident and emergency department of the nearest hospital or ring for an ambulance. Experience of mental health problems may lead to visits to or stays in a range of settings from hospital to community mental health centre to the home of a therapist. (In Unit 10 we'll be considering access to health services for drug users and homeless people who have a less settled community base.)

So while the services of some specialist practitioners are available within a domestic environment, others are found in a health centre or a hospital environment, and the need for special treatment usually means attending a hospital clinic or, if necessary, becoming a hospital inpatient. This may be because the specific expertise and equipment needed is located in one place due to economies of scale. It's just cheaper to group everything together.

In Unit 2 we saw how during this century the place of childbirth has changed. Childbirth is now more commonly a hospital-based experience, in an unfamiliar place and amongst strangers. In Doyal's chapter in the Reader, she said:

> *In most of the developed countries births have now been removed from home. Ninety-eight per cent of British women currently deliver their babies in hospital, despite the lack of compelling evidence that this is safer than a home birth (Campbell and Macfarlane, 1990). The only exception to this pattern is the Netherlands, where about a third of deliveries still take place at home. As births have been institutionalised, the hospitals themselves have also grown larger, sometimes creating an inflexible and depersonalised environment for women in labour.*
>
> *(Doyal, in the Reader)*

If you look back at the comments made to Activity 6, Unit 2, we were concerned with issues of developments in high tech medicine and the controlling influence this can have, denying 'women the opportunity to deliver their babies in the place and way they choose'. The poor home conditions which many people experienced earlier in this century provided a powerful argument in favour of hospital births, yet such conditions are no longer the case for a majority of people. Nevertheless, hospital births still dominate, although there is more shared care between hospital clinics, health centres and home.

However, it doesn't necessarily follow that all high tech equipment and specialist staff have to be located in one place. The development of primary health care services and the decentralisation from hospitals of some surgical procedures and consultant visits may mean that the health centre of the future may offer an even greater range of services. We come back to the role of health centres in Unit 10.

3.2 The hospital environment

> *Consider the surroundings of an inpatient. She/he is in a single room or multi-bedded ward furnished and equipped with the hospital bed, its bedding, overbed table, bedside locker, chairs, wheelchairs, curtains for windows and screening, light fittings, decorative finishes, vases, water jugs, wall and handset panels for emergency calls and radio programmes, notes and notices and, depending on need, items from a huge range of medical equipment – such as drip stands, medical gas cylinders and their fittings. Each of these, including the building and every item of the hospital environment, is designed by someone.*
>
> *(Scher, 1994, p. 19)*

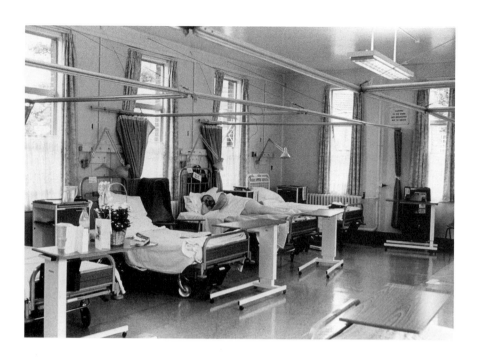

Activity 8   **The hospital environment**

Allow about 10 minutes   This quote provides us with a good visual picture of the hospital environment. Read it through several times and imagine you are a patient confined to a hospital bed. Now make some notes on how you think the physical environment of the hospital as you experience it may be different from a similar experience at home.

Comment   A bed in a ward would be surrounded by all the equipment and paraphrenalia mentioned in the quote. The furniture and furnishings would probably be uniform. There would be general lighting, noise and a lack of privacy. Flowers would perch on the overbed table and the bedside locker would probably become the most important piece of furniture as it is the only place for personal things. The experience of being in hospital would be different if you had a private room. There the scope for making it more like a bedroom would be greater.

This activity highlights the differences between home and hospital and the difficult task the hospital has in meeting the needs of patients and staff when the overriding function – providing medical care – dominates. Most people spend only brief periods of time in a general hospital and so the environment is not trying to provide a home. This will be different in settings for long-term care.

However, during recent years a number of people involved in hospital design have commented on the lack of attention paid to the views of patients and staff about the environment.

> *It is now quite clear how the requirements of technology have played a leading part in the development of modern medical practice and thereby modern hospital design. In the process, the wider and deeper range of needs of patients and staff have suffered neglect.*

> (Critchlow and Allen, 1993)

> *Somehow when patients enter hospital it is all too easy for them to*
> *experience a loss of autonomy and dignity ... Many of the most*
> *important moments of people's lives are spent in hospital yet for patients*
> *they can be cold, impersonal places.*

(Gann, 1988)

The King's Fund is an
independent health charity
based in London that carries
out a considerable amount
of research, training and
policy advice in the health
and social care field.

Instead greater attention has been paid to the technology, the cost of
building projects, and issues of safety. The King's Fund has a long
history of concern over hospital design and in 1993 held a hospital
design competition bringing together architects and other experts to
consider a number of hospitals which had been proposed as models of
good practice in design. Through talking to patients and staff and
assessing different settings, this panel of experts considered the
following to be essential for good hospital design.

> *It will be:*
> - *beautiful, or at least pleasing to the eye, and contributing*
>   *successfully to the local environment*
> - *well landscaped*
> - *easily comprehensible as a building and well signposted*
> - *easy and convenient to enter and welcoming for all patients and*
>   *visitors*
> - *finished to high standards but in styles which are non-institutional*
> - *able to offer all in-patients, and most staff, good windows with*
>   *attractive outlooks*
> - *readily and economically adaptable to meeting changing clinical*
>   *needs*
> - *efficient and convenient for the staff to provide high quality*
>   *professional care*
> - *'human', both organisationally and physically*
> - *able to provide adequate privacy and confidentiality everywhere for*
>   *patients and their relatives*
> - *designed to allow patients to control their own environments in*
>   *relation to noise, TV and radio broadcasts, ventilation and*
>   *temperature*
> - *facilitating for patients' ordinary social, intellectual and personal*
>   *lifestyles, for instance by providing adequate space, storage,*
>   *telephones and facilities for personal dietary requirements*
> - *adequately furnished for patients of all ages and types and with*
>   *sufficient WCs, bathrooms and day spaces everywhere*
> - *well designed for minorities, such as children, old or disabled people*
>   *and ethnic groups represented in the local community, and*
> - *reasonably economical in both capital and revenue terms in relation*
>   *to its own market.*

(Wickings, 1994)

If you have been in hospital at any time it might be worth pausing for a
moment to reflect on your experience of the hospital environment in the
light of these comments.

3.3 Designing for health care

In the activity which follows you become the designer. The Women's
Design Service (WDS) was asked by the Maternity Unit Mothers
Support Group (MUMS), a voluntary group which had been formed by
members of a local branch of the National Childbirth Trust, to

The Women's Design Service is a non-profit group which offers advice and consultation on the planning and design of buildings and public spaces. Its aim is to make the built environment more accessible and user-friendly for everyone.

investigate the possibility of a new calling system to aid staff at the antenatal clinic at Whipps Cross Hospital in London and to recommend low-cost improvement to the waiting area. Together they carried out a survey by questionnaire among 66 women in different clinics over a two-week period, consulting women on their views of the waiting area and the time they spent there. They also held interviews with midwives about the organisation of the clinic. In addition six other antenatal clinics in London hospitals were visited as part of the research. Some of the findings are given in a moment. First, what would be important to you in these circumstances?

Activity 9

Allow about 15 minutes

Thinking about waiting

Imagine you are a pregnant woman and have been waiting for at least an hour in the following setting. You have an appointment but you are not sure with whom and you have your three-year-old son with you. Make some notes about the types of things which you feel would improve this environment.

The waiting area is essentially long and narrow, with nine doors leading to consulting rooms situated along one side. There is no indication on the door as to which member of staff is using which room.

There is currently a children's play area near the window, consisting mainly of a play-house. Although this section has the advantage of greater natural light and of having a view of outside, those sitting here are even further away from the consulting rooms and are not likely to hear their names being called. Those waiting to have their blood tested, who also sit in this area, are similarly at a disadvantage.

The overall impression of the clinic is affected by the low lighting level. Since the windows are situated out of sight from reception, the natural light that they provide does not benefit the area as a whole.

The women are called by the midwives shouting names from the doorways of the consulting rooms.

(Women's Design Service, 1991, p. 9)

Waiting for care

Comments   One of our course testers made these comments:

> *I thought that I would be concerned about a number of things. I would be most anxious about keeping my son occupied. It is likely that there will be a lot of children and they would need a variety of things to play with. Then I would be concerned about hearing my name being called and knowing where to go. Also, I'd probably need to go to the toilet and then I'd be worried that I would miss my turn whilst I was out of earshot. I'd want something comfortable to sit on and if I hadn't brought anything to do with me, I'd want something to read. The lighting might be a problem as it sounds dark and gloomy. Oh, yes ... I'd also probably want a drink or my son would, especially if I had to wait for ages.*

So what did the women say who were interviewed in the research? Here are some of their main comments:

- it felt overcrowded and noisy
- there weren't enough facilities for children
- the calling system did not work
- there was a lack of information about clinic procedure
- the WRVS canteen only stayed open until 3.30 p.m.
- there was little to read
- there was nowhere to breastfeed privately
- there was a need for more toys and books for children
- there was no supervision of the children's play area
- there were no signs to the men's toilets
- the seating was uncomfortable.

On the basis of this study the WDS went on to write their own broadsheet which they recommend as a supplement to Department of Health guidelines on the design of these kinds of units (WDS, 1993). Their aim has been to provide an environment that is informative and enables the user to understand what is going and then allows them 'to wait in a comfortable, well-lit, friendly environment equipped with basic facilities such as clean toilets (including a nappy changing unit) and refreshments.' (WDS, 1991, p. 3.)

Although designing a new clinic might be costly, many of the recommendations made here could be put into practice quite quickly without too much expense *and* are the direct result of consultation. If we changed the scenario to consider the needs of a retired man with failing sight who comes for an x-ray, then some of the issues raised here would also be important, though greater emphasis may be placed on sign-posting and call systems.

The hospital environment has to meet different needs from the home environment. In particular, as with many special care settings, the design has to be both a living environment for patients or residents, and a working environment for staff. The hospital setting also has to accommodate a wide range of equipment and technology. Even so, as we saw in the last activity both design and organisational practice in hospitals can create disabling environments causing unnecessary discomfort.

Key points

- Health care can take place in a range of domestic and specialised settings.

- Sometimes health needs which could be met at home are located in hospital.

- The hospital environment has to meet competing needs of patients, staff and technology.

- Taking on board the views of users and staff can improve environments.

Section 4
Setting the scene for care

We've established that there are a range of places where people give and receive care and that the physical environment (in terms of buildings) as well as the social environment (in terms of the ways people use places) can influence people's experiences.

Housing in the main is designed for the 'family' but as we began to see in Unit 1, family forms vary and change over time. So *who* lives *where* and *with whom* will have a bearing on how care relationships develop, whether services are needed at home, and whether the barriers to being able to live at home are just too great.

Because we are going to look at this broad picture, this section continues the work on number skills which you began in Unit 1. To help you we will also be continuing your reading of Chapter 4 of *The Good Study Guide*, 'Working with numbers'.

Statistics and data

Statistics are items of information expressed in numbers. (Look back quickly at the box on p. 90 of *The Good Study Guide*.) Statistical information is collected for a variety of purposes: census data, survey data (at national and local levels) and routine annual returns. Much of this information is collected through surveys. National surveys are carried out with *samples* of people who represent a larger *population*. (You read about populations in the note at the bottom of p. 94 of *The Good Study Guide*.) Information is generally gathered by asking people questions. But of course, *how* questions are worded, *who* is asked, and how the results are *analysed* can make a lot of difference to the figures, so we must always be cautious in interpreting statistics.

A lot of the official statistical sources give data for Britain, i.e. England, Wales and Scotland, but not Northern Ireland, although this is included in the United Kingdom data. (A *datum* is an item of information. The plural – *data* – means many items of information.) Here we will be looking at data collected through the national Census (carried out every 10 years) and the General Household Survey (a sample survey of the general population which began in 1971). We have taken some of these data from the publication *Social Trends* which brings together a range of statistics on aspects of everyday life. It is published every year by the Office for National Statistics. You should be able to find a copy in your local library. Have a look next time you visit.

4.1 Who do people live with?

When it comes to thinking about who people live with it is common to talk about 'households' – those people who occupy the same house or dwelling. But what exactly is a household? We have already looked at 'families' in Unit 1, but households are different. For one thing the occupants may or may not be related by blood, marriage or ties of affection.

When the Census was taken in 1991, the definition of household used was as follows:

> *A household is defined as one person living alone or a group of persons (not necessarily related) living at the same address with common housekeeping – that is sharing at least one meal a day or sharing a living room or sitting room.*
>
> *(OPCS, 1993a, p. 2, para 4.3)*

Notice that this definition relates people to activities such as 'common housekeeping', eating together, the preparation of food, and to sharing space within accommodation. This helps to distinguish a household from what is described as a 'communal establishment'.

> *Establishments where some form of communal catering was provided, such as hotels, boarding houses, hospitals, homes etc., were enumerated on different forms from those used for households, and statistics on these, including persons sleeping rough, are included in a separate report on* **communal establishments***.*
>
> *(OPCS, 1993a, p. 2, para 4.3)*

These are important distinctions, when we are talking about statistics. People are divided into categories on the basis of criteria such as these, statistics being collected separately for people living in households and people living in communal establishments or without a household at all. So we have a definition of 'household' along these lines:

household = people + activities + space

Being a part of a household gives people an identity, a location, an address. And just as registering with a family doctor is a key to receiving health care, so being part of a household also opens up the potential for receiving social care. As we shall see in Block 3, being homeless can create problems with access to care services.

So what do households look like? If you think about *people you know* you can probably identify quite a range of different types.

Activity 10   **People and households**

Allow about 10 minutes   Jot down as many different types of households as come to mind. Then write down what you think is the size of the average household in Britain or Northern Ireland.

Comment   The different types of household used in the 1991 Census included:

- couples without children
- couples with child(ren)
- people living alone
- more than two adults sharing
- one adult with child(ren).

In Britain in 1994–95, there were 23.1 million households for a population of 56.8 million. If we 'round' these figures then 57 divided by 23 gives an average household of about 2.5 people.

Does this figure surprise you in any way? If you thought that the average household might contain four or five people then you would expect the number of households for a population of 56.8 million to be much smaller, say 14 million. In fact, the average household size in Britain has almost halved during the twentieth century from 4.6 to 2.5 persons (Haskey, 1996). And as we saw in Unit 1, contrary to popular stereotypes, not every family consists of two adults + two children. But of course, the figures hide a wide range of different household sizes and types.

Figures for Northern Ireland show that the average household size is slightly larger than in Britain at 2.9 people. A greater number of households contain five or six people, and a greater proportion include children aged 0–4 years (Department of Health and Social Services, Registrar General Northern Ireland, 1993).

But is defining households as easy as that and how do definitions such as these relate to matters of caring?

Activity 11	Who is in the household?
Allow about 5 minutes	Read the following description and then, *using the definition of a household given above,* write down who you think is in Maureen's household. By the way, you will be meeting Maureen again in Unit 7.

Maureen is a registered childminder who lives in a three-bedroomed terraced house. She shares the house with her partner Pat and their son, Aidan aged 12 years, her unmarried daughter Tracy aged 21 years (from her first marriage) and Tracy's son Jo (three years). They have three cats and a dog. Maureen looks after a boy of three years six months who she cares for full-time, her grandson Jo – while Tracey is working – and three children whom she cares for after nursery and school.

Comment   Difficult isn't it? According to the census definition given above, for part of the day at least, all of the adults and children mentioned here could be said to be of one household. Yet a number of the children come from different families and go to back to their own homes each day. Are the children who are not members of the family part of the household? I decided to focus on those who lived and slept in the house. I thought that Maureen and Pat were a couple with children except for the fact that Maureen's daughter, Tracy, also has a child. Are they another household or another family? They could be seen as another household, although Maureen describes everyone as 'just part of the family'.

So relationships between families and households are not as straightforward as the definitions may imply and this is something to bear in mind when considering the statistics.

Haskey (1996), in a review of changes and trends within families and households in Britain during the twentieth century, tells us that 'families were not satisfactorily distinguished from households in censuses until 1961' and that this was because 'during the last century and the early part of the present one, many households contained members of the extended family, as defined by blood or marriage, in addition to those of the nuclear family'. The present definition of a nuclear family, as we saw in Unit 1, spans only two generations, so Maureen's is an extended family.

4.2 Changing households

Of course, households and family forms change over time. Table 1 shows us the most recent changes.

> ### Study skills: Reading tables
>
> The information in Table 1 is extremely useful to anyone interested in policies on care provision in the home. It also gives you a chance to practise the skills in table reading which you began to work on in Block 1. If, as we suggested, you completed Section 3 of Chapter 4 of *The Good Study Guide*, you should find the next activity quite straightforward, though it would be worth going back to remind yourself of the key points on table reading on p. 98.
>
> You are going to meet quite a few numbers in this section so expect to take a little time over it. You don't need to 'memorise' all the numbers, but it will be very useful to get a sense of the general 'shape' of things. It is an important part of your skills building in K100 to use this as a chance to develop your confidence and your technique in extracting the essence from numbers you meet.

Table 1   Composition of households, by type of household and family, 1961–94, Britain

Type of household	1961 %	1994 %	Differences %
One person households			
Under pensionable age	4	12	+8
Over pensionable age	7	15	+8
Two or more related adults	5	3	-2
Married couples with:			
No children	26	27	+1
1–2 dependent children[†]	30	20	-10
3 or more dependent children[†]	8	5	-3
Non-dependent children only	10	6	-4
Lone parent with:			
Dependent children[†]	2	7	+5
Non-dependent children	4	3	-1
Two or more families	3	1	-2
Number of households in millions	16.2	23.1	+6.9

[†] Dependent children are defined as: persons aged 0–15 in a household; or persons aged 16–18, never married, in full-time education and economically inactive. These households may also include non-dependent children.

(Source: Censuses, and 1994 General Household Survey from Haskey, 1996)

Activity 12   **Changing households**

Allow about 10 minutes for each section of this activity

(a)   Take some time to study this table. The types of household listed here are more detailed than those given in Activity 10. They are presented here as percentages of the total number of households.

Try to answer the following questions:

(i)   What does the '4' at the top of the first column tell us?

(ii) In 1961, what percentage of households were one person households?

(iii) What does the '16.2' at the bottom of the first column tell us?

Comment (i) The '4' is a percentage. It tells us that 4 per cent of all households in 1961 consisted of one person under pensionable age.

(ii) The table divides one person households into two types. In the first the person was under pensionable age and in the second over pensionable age. We have already seen that in 1961 4 per cent of households were single person households of the first type, and we can also see that 7 per cent were single person households of the second type. To answer the question we need to add these two together: 4 + 7 = 11. So, in 1961, 11 per cent of households had just one person.

(iii) If we look to the left of the 16.2, we can see it is the total number of households (of all types), in millions. In other words there were 16,200,000 households in 1961.

Allow about 10 minutes (b) Since we are interested in changes, we want to know the differences between the figures for 1961 and 1994. Look at the column on the right where +8 is written in. This is to show that the proportion of households of one person under pensionable age rose by 8 per cent (the difference between 4 and 12). If you go down to the next row the change is from 7 to 15. If you subtract 7 from 15, you can see that again there is an increase of 8, so you can write in +8.

Go down the rest of the column writing in the differences between the two figures. Remember to put a minus sign if the figure has fallen.

Comment (b) The figures in the right hand column should now be: +8, +8, -2, +1, -10, -3, -4, +5, -1, -2, +6.9.

Allow about 10 minutes (c) Now you are in a position to assess the changes. Look down the differences column to find which are the main increases and which the decreases.

(i) Has there been an increase or a decrease between 1961 and 1994 in the proportion of households of each of the following types:

• married couples with three or more dependent children

• lone parents with dependent children

• married couples with no children?

(ii) What types of household show the most change over the past 30 years?

Comment (c) How did you get on?

(i) There has been:

• a decrease in the proportion of households with married couples with three or more dependent children

• an increase in the proportion of households with lone parents with dependent children

• little change in the proportion of households with married couples with no children.

(ii)   We can see that there have been big rises in the proportions of households with only one person and with a lone parent with dependent children. And we can see that there has been a sharp fall in the proportion of households with 1–2 dependent children (from 3 in every 10 to 2 in every 10). However, we must also notice that there has been a big increase in the total number of households (because there are fewer people in each household). (This means, for example, that although the proportion of lone parent households with non-dependent children has dropped slightly, the actual number of such households has increased.)

Of course, reading a table like this doesn't tell us anything about *why* these changes are happening.

Activity 13   Changing households – reasons

Allow about 10 minutes   Look at the differences column in Table 1 again and think about why these changes may have taken place. Using what you already know about your society write down as many ideas as you can. If you live in Northern Ireland some of the major trends shown here will also apply but others may vary. Try to think how the picture might be similar or different in Northern Ireland.

Comment   Some of the main demographic changes to impact upon families and households in twentieth century Britain are summarised in the box below. Read it carefully, and compare the changes here with your own impressions. Try to think whether they match what you've seen happening around you. Don't try to memorise the list itself *but remember where it is*. You may wish to check back to it from time to time.

Changes in families and households in the twentieth century

- Growth in population.
- Fall in fertility [i.e.] trends towards older age at childbearing and increasing childlessness.
- Advent of modern contraception and increased use of abortion.
- Smaller household and family sizes.
- Decline in extended families and multi-family households; fewer kin.
- Virtual disappearance of domestic servants; considerable reduction in lodgers.
- Growth in living alone.
- Fall in infant mortality, resulting in virtually all children surviving to adulthood.
- Decline in adult mortality; lower prevalence of widowed lone parenthood and increased proportions of families spanning two, three or more generations.
- Increased numbers of elderly people who either live alone, in institutions or with their children or relatives.
- Decline in adoption and growth of single lone motherhood.

- Increase in extra-marital fertility and consequent growth in cohabiting couple families and lone parenthood.

- Rise in prevalence of cohabitation, decline in first marriage, growth in divorce.

- Increase in the proportion of remarriages amongst all marriages; increase in 'reconstituted' families and stepfamilies.

- Growth in lone parent cohabitation (with new partners); creation of cohabiting couple stepfamilies.

- Immigration, particularly after World War II and during the 1960s.

- Growth in the size of the ethnic minority populations resulting in greater heterogeneity in family sizes, household composition, and kinship patterns.

- Differential fertility, mortality and migration rates in the various regions ... resulting in geographical variation in population growth and family structures.

(Haskey, 1996)

Reading through this list it may have struck you that many of the changes are interrelated – for example the fall in fertility, the advent of modern contraception and the growth in smaller household and family sizes.

But figures and trends described in this way only give a general view of what is going on within one country. There can be enormous variations in different places. For example, as mentioned earlier, census data show that households in Northern Ireland tend to be larger than those in Britain. Figures show that 'in 1994–95 around 15 per cent had five or more members which was about twice the proportion in Great Britain' (Office for National Statistics, 1996). Data also show that families of the Catholic religion tend to live in larger households than those who describe themselves as Protestant. This is largely due to the higher number of children under 16 years of age in Catholic households which is partly due to attitudes towards birth control contraception. Overall, however, the birth rate in Northern Ireland is falling.

One of the most striking things in looking at the table and reading the list is the increase in the number of people living alone in one-person households. You began to look at this in Unit 1, but you can learn more about who lives alone by looking at the bar charts given overleaf.

Study skills: Reading a bar chart

Reading bar charts and pie charts is generally easier than reading tables, since their whole purpose is to make numbers easy to take in. However, you need to spend a little time just finding your way around, to get the feel of what the shapes are telling. You have already worked with pie charts in Unit 1 and a bar chart in Unit 3. Now it is worth building up a general technique for approaching charts. Section 4.1 of Chapter 4 of *The Good Study Guide* offers some guidance on reading charts and a list of tips. Read it before going on to Activity 14.

Activity 14 Living alone

Allow about 10 minutes

The bars in this chart represent percentages of men and women living alone in different age groups for two different years. Study the bar chart and write down two things it tells you.

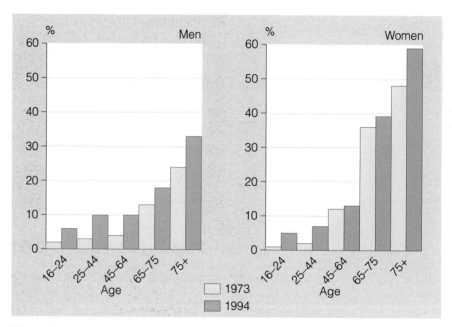

Figure 1
Proportions of men and women who live alone, 1973 and 1994, Britain (General Household Survey in Haskey, 1996)

Comment

(a) The most dramatic thing about this bar chart is the fact that there is a much higher proportion of women over 65 years of age living alone and that this group has increased over the 25 year period, especially for those over 75. A majority of older women, 6 out of 10, were living alone in 1994, compared to 3 out of 10 men. These trends reflect the fact that women live longer than men and therefore, if married, are more likely to experience widowhood.

(b) Another interesting change shown by the figure is the substantial increase in the numbers of men in the 25–44 age group living alone. This may reflect a whole host of things including employment patterns, the rise in separation and divorce, and the increase in age of marriage.

Official statistics can also begin to tell us something of the diversity that exists between different groups of people.

Activity 15 Reflecting diversity

Allow about 10 minutes

The following data are given in the form of pie charts. Here each of the pies represents different minority ethnic groupings and the pie is divided up on the basis of different household size (using definitions from the Labour Force Survey in 1995). Look at the diagrams and write down two things which strike you.

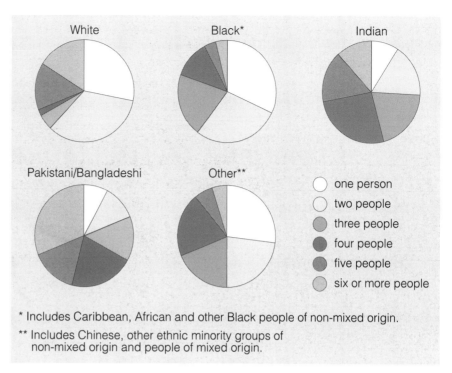

Figure 2
Ethnic group of head of household by household size, Spring 1995 (Office for National Statistics, 1996, Table 2.5, p. 51)

Comment   You might have reached any of the following conclusions:

- the Pakistani/Bangladeshi ethnic group has the largest group of households of six or more people

- almost one-third of people from the Black ethnic group live alone

- those from the white ethnic group are most likely to have households of either one or two people

- Asian groups, Indian, Pakistani/Bangladeshi groupings have a large number of four person households.

The differences shown here might lead us to draw certain conclusions about household size and meeting care needs. For example it is often assumed that, as Asian households are more likely to be extended families than others in Britain, then family support and care may be easier to organise. But survey data also show us that households from the Pakistani/Bangladeshi ethnic group have on average more children under 16 years. And other research has shown that traditional Asian family patterns have changed over time and that the nuclear family is now more common (Blakemore and Boneham, 1994). So family support and care for older generations cannot be assumed. While the data show us there are differences, we have to be very cautious in drawing conclusions. (We will be looking more closely at the type of services and support received by different groups within society in Block 3.)

On the other hand, it is very clear that different household structures will have a marked effect on the availability of people to offer care or support to each other.

> **Key points**
>
> - The official definition of a 'household' takes into account sharing of space and housekeeping arrangements.
> - There are a variety of household types.
> - Over time household size has been getting smaller – so there are more people living alone.
> - There are differences within and between regions.
> - Household patterns change over time and this is true for all groups including different ethnic groups. However, we should beware of stereotypes in interpreting data for different groups.
> - Household structures affect who is available to care.

4.3 Who is there to care?

Patterns of living have changed over time and this has a direct impact on whether there is an informal family network available to care for someone in need of assistance. One important factor which doesn't appear in our figures here is that many family members no longer live near to each other. Moving, both within the home country and between countries, has become a part of life. This is often called 'geographical mobility'. Some people move away from their place of origin in order to find employment. Others make a move at times in their lives such as retirement. In addition divorce, separation and remarriage can cause family members of different generations to become separated.

Activity 16

Allow about 10 minutes

Living apart

Read the following case study and consider how family change and living apart might affect the capacity for family members to help each other. In particular think about the older people mentioned here, their changing circumstances and how they might meet any care needs in the future.

Bill

Bill lives with his two teenage daughters in Newcastle.

He runs his own dry-cleaning business. At the age of 52 years he became a widower. His mother-in-law from his first marriage, Betty aged 75, lives nearby. She had relied on Jean, her daughter, for some basic shopping and help with other household tasks.

After Jean's death Bill carried on helping his mother-in-law with the assistance of his two daughters. However, Jo the youngest starts college this year, and Sam is getting married in six month's time. Betty has one other daughter, Jenny, who lives in Wales and has recently been divorced. She visits occasionally. Bill's own parents, Ida and Sid, live in a sheltered housing scheme in Exeter. His sister June lives near by. Two years ago Bill met Pat, aged 54, and they married a month ago. Pat's father is a widower who lives on his own in Bedford. She is increasingly worried about how he is coping on his own, especially as she is his only child.

Comment The older people in this scenario all live in different places. Sid and Ida live in sheltered housing. They are the furthest away from Bill but they live near his sister. Bill's commitment to his mother-in-law may now become strained given that his new wife, Pat, obviously feels she would like to do more for her father. However, Bill does have his business to consider. He may not want to move to be near his new father-in-law.

This brief scenario begins to tell us something about the complex relationships between employment patterns, distance from kin, gender and caring responsibilities, the impact of family break-down and reconstitution on caring, and the consideration of alternative forms of accommodation and care in later life. These are common concerns in many families today. There are no simple solutions but they can have an important bearing not only on who is there to care but where care takes place.

Life gets complex

Caring from within or without

The degree to which family members live near to, or far away from, each other is obviously one important factor in who provides informal care. But another important distinction is whether the carer actually lives in the same household as the care receiver, sometimes called *co-resident care*, or whether they live apart, sometimes called *non-resident care*.

The data on households showed us that more older women than older men live on their own. More older men are likely to live with their partner.

Arber and Ginn (1991) have explored older people's preferences for how and where they receive care, and from whom. In their estimation staying in your own home and being cared for by someone who does not live with you is preferred to moving in with a carer. Self-care, or spouse care, are the preferred options for most older people and there is evidence that if people are not living with a spouse and they have care needs then they increasingly prefer the support of formal carers (Ackers and Abbott, 1996; Phillipson, 1990).

The distinction between co-resident and non-resident care is important because research shows that there is an enormous difference between the two in the amount of care undertaken. Co-resident carers, not surprisingly, spend far more time caring than those who don't (Arber and Ginn, 1991). As we saw in Block 1, Lynne was a resident carer and the fact that she lived with her father and had never been able to break away from this home environment placed greater responsibility upon her to care.

Key points

- It is more common now for family members to live apart from each other and this affects the availability of people to care for each other.

- Care can be provided by someone who is co-resident and lives with the care receiver or someone who is non-resident and lives apart. This affects the level and type of care provided.

4.4 Resources for care

While statistics show that there has been an overall increase in household income during the 1980s and early 1990s, they also tell us that the gap between the 'haves' and the 'have nots' has been increasing. 'The proportion of people with incomes below half the average increased from 8 per cent in 1982 to just over 20 per cent by 1992, since when it has fallen slightly' (Office for National Statistics, 1997, p. 89). Cash payments provided by the State (through Income Support and other allowances) define a minimum level of income and people living below this level have been termed by researchers and policy analysts as 'living in poverty'. Not surprisingly, the people who fall into this category include older people, the low paid, unemployed people, lone-parent families and people with long-term sickness or disabilities (Jones, 1994). People from ethnic minority groups are also over-represented among low income households.

Many people on the receiving end of the care services discussed in this course fall into low income categories and are reliant on a range of state benefits to meet their needs. Many people with disabilities either experience difficulty in finding paid employment or are unable to work, and some retired people find life on the state pension one of subsistence poverty – not having sufficient income to meet their basic needs. Older people form the largest group of benefit recipients. Yet amongst older people the income gap is also widening. On one side are those with additional occupational pensions, predominantly men and, on the other, those who live on the basic state provision, predominantly women.

Inequality of resources is fundamental to the discussion of accommodation and care. During the past 50 years the emphasis within housing policy has swung dramatically. In the post-war period the dominant themes were slum clearance, reconstruction and providing housing for families through the development of council housing. Then in the 1980s there was a move towards privatisation and the promotion of owner-occupation as a preferred form of housing tenure. The graph in Figure 3 shows this dramatic shift. There has also been a gradual decline in renting from local authorities and a gradual increase in property rented from housing associations.

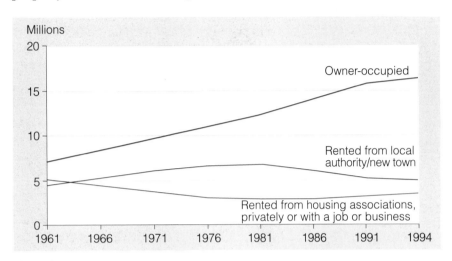

Figure 3
Housing stock at December each year by tenure, UK (Office for National Statistics, 1997, Figure 10.1, p. 169)

Once again this is a very general picture. Here are just some of the things the graph does not tell us:

- more than two-thirds of those heads of households aged under 25 years live in rented accommodation

- amongst those heads of households over 60 years of age over half own their own home outright – without a mortgage

- eight per cent of those over 80 years, predominantly older women, live in private rented accommodation mostly in the inner cities

- African-Caribbean households are more likely to be renting from local authorities and housing associations than any other group.

(Office for National Statistics, 1996, 1997.)

These statistics give us a glimpse of the wide variation in the impact of home ownership on people's lives. The push towards owner-occupation has been based on the expectation that a house can be a financial asset. However, changes in the housing market can make home ownership a bonus for some and a nightmare for others. Housing costs vary enormously throughout the country. Some people can find that they cannot afford to meet their mortgage repayments; others that they are faced with negative equity – their property being no longer worth what they paid for it. Regarding care, perhaps the most important issue to emerge for older people and their families is the way assessments of their housing assets are now made when 'paying for long term care' in both residential care and nursing homes. This has led to political concerns over the transfer of wealth between the generations, and the cost of long-term care (Peace et al. 1997). One result has been a raising of the level of assets below which individuals are entitled to receive public funding. In April 1996 this rose from £8,000 to £16,000.

Housing: asset or liability?

Although a house is often seen as an asset it may also form an obstacle to care. In terms of housing conditions very few households now lack basic amenities: less than one per cent lack facilities such as a bath/shower or an internal flushing toilet, and the vast majority of accommodation now has central heating, although this is less true of the private rented sector. The housing conditions of the majority of older people have improved since the mid-1980s (Department of Environment, 1993) and yet for some conditions remain very poor.

Housing circumstances have become a major reason for seeking alternative accommodation which meets care needs. For example older people moving into sheltered housing schemes often do so in their mid-70s because their housing no longer meets their needs. It may be too big, have stairs they cannot manage, be in need of repair, or have a garden that is too big to handle. In fact, their accommodation needs may be more pressing than their care needs even though they may anticipate them. In contrast, older people moving into residential care homes more commonly do so at a later age when they have been living alone in their own homes, with multiple physical and/or mental health problems and are already in receipt of home care services (Peace *et al.*, 1997).

The poor circumstances in which some people live has a direct impact on their health and well-being. The link between housing and health is well established (Ineichen, 1993). Here we can touch only briefly upon the inequalities which exist between people in terms of income and the impact this may have for housing need. If you look back to Section 2.4 and the comments made by Hudson *et al.* (1996) financial constraints were seen as one of the barriers to finding accommodation for people with care needs. Morris and Winn (1991) put it like this:

> *There are three aspects to housing situation which can be seen when measuring housing inequality. Firstly, there are the issues of access to housing, security of tenure and opportunities for mobility; that is, whether someone is able to get the housing they need, and once they have it, to be secure in their occupancy. Then there are the physical characteristics of the home which are important dimensions of advantage and disadvantage – space, number of rooms, heating and insulation, state of repair, environment surrounding the home and so on. Finally, some people enjoy opportunities of access to credit and capital as a result of their housing situation while others do not.*
>
> *(pp. 1–2)*

Key points

- Inequalities over resources is fundamental to the discussion of accommodation and care.

- The growth of owner-occupation has made housing a financial asset for more people, but creates problems for some.

- Housing tenure, type and condition varies widely and can critically affect care options.

4.5 People who need accommodation and care

This unit began by considering the physical environment provided by domestic homes – the most common places for care. It went on to explore some of the reasons why people with social or health care needs might find themselves in special settings including hospitals and what might be done to make these environments more people friendly. This last section of Unit 6 has focused on some facts about accommodation which provide a background for understanding how care is affected by people's circumstances. In looking at definitions of households we were reminded that not everyone lives in one; some people live in communal establishments or without a household at all. To end, we return to some facts about people who receive accommodation and/or care services.

Study skills: Coping with the figures

You have already met a lot of figures in this section of Unit 6. Perhaps you are beginning to feel overwhelmed? What are you supposed to do with them? You certainly couldn't expect to remember them all unless you have a very special kind of memory.

In fact, you don't need to have the actual figures in your head. You can always look them up again if you need them. The point is to get a general idea of the scale of things, the proportions, the broad trends. In many cases you will already have had an impression of how things are, but seeing the figures gives you a chance to check whether you were in the right general area, or whether your impression was way off. The final activity is set up to do just that. We ask you to make some guesses and see how close your existing picture of things is. You will also pick up some clues as to where to look for figures of this kind.

But if you feel you are flagging, don't let these figures get you down. You are near the end of the most concentrated burst of number work in K100. Just take what you can for now and come back later if you need to. It is important that you gradually become familiar with some basic facts and figures, but it is also important to keep up your spirits.

Perhaps the first question to ask is how many children and adults actually live in care settings such as residential homes or hostels? Guessing the answers to questions like this is pretty difficult, although it's quite a useful exercise. I certainly didn't know all the answers to the questions set out below and I had to consult a lot of official sources to try and piece together the current picture. I discovered that less than 2 per cent of the British population were resident in some form of communal setting, such as a hospital or residential home when the 1991 population census took place. In Northern Ireland the figure was 1.5 per cent of the population.

Activity 17   **In need of care and accommodation**

Allow a few minutes for each section of this activity

This activity is presented as a series of questions with feedback given as you go along. Don't worry if you don't know the answers. We are only after a guess here; it is not a test of knowledge.

(a)   In the United Kingdom there were about 12.5 million children and young people under the age of 18 years in 1994. How many do you think live in children's homes?
- 2 per cent
- less than 1 per cent
- 3 per cent

Comment   (a)   In England, Wales and Northern Ireland the numbers of children and young people looked after by, or in the care of, local authorities, fell by 44 per cent between 1981 and 1994 from 99,000 to 55,000. The proportion of these living with foster parents increased over this period from two-fifths to three-fifths. In 1994, 34,100 lived with foster parents and 7,150 lived in homes run by local authorities and the voluntary sector. Scotland has a different definition of children in care which includes 'children who are under a non-residential supervision requirement from a children's hearing'. In 1994 there were 12,000 children in care in Scotland (Office for National Statistics, 1997, p. 150) but the 1991 Census shows that only 996 children under 18 years were resident in children's homes. If we piece together this information then around 8,000 children are living in homes out of a total population of 12,500,000. If we express the 8,000 as a percentage of the total population, then the answer is *less than* 1 per cent.

Allow a few minutes (b) What percentage of people between the ages of 65 and 74 years do you think live in residential care or nursing homes? Is it:
- 10 per cent
- 3 per cent
- 2 per cent

Comment (b) Figures for 1995 show that there were 301,400 residential home places and 208,000 nursing home places in the UK, a majority provided by the private sector (56 per cent residential, 92 per cent nursing) (Laing, 1996). Figures from the 1991 Census for Britain show that around 1 per cent of people aged 65–74 years were resident in residential care and nursing homes at that time (though it was 3 per cent of those defined as having a 'long term limiting illness') (OPCS, 1993b and c). This percentage remains relatively consistent across England, Scotland and Wales. In Northern Ireland the figure is also approximately 1 per cent. The answer to the question is therefore *less than* 2 per cent.

Allow a few minutes (c) What percentage of people 85 years and over do you think live in residential care or nursing homes? Is it:
- 35 per cent
- 25 per cent
- 10 per cent

Comment (c) Using the same Census data we find that in Britain 21 per cent of people over 85 years were resident in residential care and nursing homes on Census night (though it was 30 per cent for people having a 'long term limiting illness'). These figures are relatively similar in England and Wales, though in Scotland the percentage was lower (17 per cent) and in Northern Ireland 19 per cent (Department of Health and Social Services, Registrar General Northern Ireland, 1993). Laing, in his market survey of 'Care of Elderly People', estimates that 26 per cent of the population over 85 years of age can expect to live in some form of care setting. *So the nearest answer to this question is 25 per cent* (Laing, 1996).

Allow a few minutes (d) How many people are currently 'homeless'?

Comment   (d)   There are no national figures for the total number of people who are homeless and in housing need. Statistics quoted in official publications are for the number of 'officially' homeless households – that is those entitled to a home from a local authority or housing association under existing legislation regarding homelessness. In July 1993, 139,790 households were accepted as homeless by councils in England, and Shelter, the charity which campaigns for homeless people, estimated that this represented about 401,000 homeless individuals (Butler *et al.*, 1994; Shelter, 1994).

Those with a priority need are commonly offered temporary accommodation such as bed and breakfast hotels, hostels and short-life leasing accommodation until the local authority can find them permanent accommodation. In 1994 in Britain there were 52,000 households living in temporary accommodation, although the use of bed and breakfast hotels had fallen by two-thirds since 1991. The most common type of temporary accommodation is short-life leasing. For those not in a priority category such as a majority of young people, local authorities can help by securing accommodation or providing advice and assistance to enable them to find accommodation themselves.

How did you get on? Was it what you expected? These figures show us that a majority of people who may need some form of care live in ordinary housing within the community. For example you can see that the popular myth that 'most older people live in residential care homes' just isn't true: most older people live in their own homes. The figures for children living in residential homes are relatively small but this reflects changes in policy towards placing children with foster families rather than in residential homes.

But although a majority of people who may need care live in housing within the community, the figures also tell us that some people need both accommodation and care services. Indeed as people get older the chance that they might live in some form of non-domestic setting increases. Equally homeless families, whose most visible and urgent need is for accommodation, often (because of their situation) also have care needs. The two are inextricably intertwined.

The reasons why some adults and children live in care settings while others, who may have similar needs, do not are complex. They include family resources (both personal and financial); state social policy and allocation of resources; and society's attitudes to different groups of people who are seen to have 'special needs'. Moreover, all these factors interact and change over time. We will be looking in more detail at the lives of people who live in residential care in Unit 8.

Key points

- For a majority of people their needs for both health and social care are met at home.

- The numbers of people who live in communal establishments or care settings is relatively small.

- However, as people get older their chance of living in a non-domestic setting increases.

- The number of people living in different kinds of care setting is often a reflection of the social policies of the time.

Conclusion

In this unit, I have explored where care takes place and at this point you might wish to look back at the core questions set at the beginning of the unit. I began by focusing on the domestic home as the centre of family life and the place of most care relationships. The design of family housing has evolved over time and taken account of certain ideas about the family which relate to issues of gender roles and culture.

We have also seen that the physical environment of the home can be disabling and that a failure to meet accommodation needs can lead to the marrying of accommodation and care within special care settings which often segregate some groups from others.

The most specialised of care settings is the hospital and here the demands of both living and working environments come into stark relief. What aspects of ordinary domestic housing and home life can be incorporated within settings which specialise in the delivery of care?

The changing nature of households and living arrangements has an impact on care and support. Yet, although accommodation and care are intimately entwined, they deserve to be considered separately. Receiving care in a place which can be called home says a lot about the sense of control people have over their lives. In Unit 7, I move on to look at the meanings we attach to home, how we use the spaces we live in, and how we make the transitions between different places in order to give and receive care.

Study skills: Review of number work skills

In this unit you have practised some very useful and important skills in reading tables and diagrams. Now that you have reached the end of the unit, it is a good time to consolidate those skills. One way of doing this is to complete your reading of Chapter 4 of *The Good Study Guide* (you have already read most of it). Then you will be equipped for reading any other tables and diagrams you meet in the course.

References

Ackers, L. and Abbott, P. (1996) *Social Policy for Nurses and the Caring Professions*, Open University Press, Buckingham.

Arber, S. and Ginn, J (1991) *Gender and Later Life – A Sociological Analysis of Resources and Constraints*, Sage Publications Ltd, London.

Blakemore, K. and Boneham, M. (1994) *Age, Race and Ethnicity: A Comparative Approach*, Open University Press, Buckingham.

Bulter, K., Carlisle, B. and Lloyd, R. (1994) *Homelessness in the 1990s: Local Authority Practice*, Shelter, London.

Critchlow, K. and Allen, J. (1993) 'The whole question of health', report to the King's Fund, London.

Davidoff, L., l'Esperance, L. and Newby, H. (1976) 'Landscape with figures: home and community in English society' in Mitchell, J. and Oakley, A. (eds) *The Rights and Wrongs of Women*, Penguin, Harmondsworth, pp. 139–75.

Department of Environment (1993) *English Housing Condition Survey 1991*, HMSO, London.

Department of Health and Social Services, Registrar General Northern Ireland (1993) *The Northern Ireland Census 1991: Housing and Household Composition Report*, HMSO, Belfast.

Doyal, L. (1995) *What Makes Women Sick*, Macmillan, Basingstoke.

Foo, B. (1984) 'House and home', in Matrix (eds) *Making Space: Women and the Man Made Environment*, Pluto Press, London.

Gann, R. (1988) 'What your patients may be reading', *British Medical Journal*, Vol. 296, pp. 493–5.

Garmarnikow, E., Morgan, D., Purvis, J. and Taylorson, D. (eds) (1983) *The Public and the Private*, Heinemann, London.

Haskey, J. (1996) 'Population review (6) Families and households in Great Britain', *Population Trends*, No. 85, Autumn, pp. 7–24.

Hudson, J., Watson, L. and Allan, G. (1996) *Moving Obstacles: Housing Choices and Community Care*, The Policy Press, Bristol.

Ineichen, B. (1993) *Homes and Health. How Housing and Health Interact*, E & F Spon, London.

Jones, L. (1994) *The Social Control of Health and Health Work*, Macmillan, Basingstoke.

Joseph Rowntree Foundation (1997) *Foundations: Building Lifetime Homes*, Joseph Rowntree Foundation, York.

Laing, W. (1996) *Laing's Review of Private Healthcare 1996*, Laing and Buisson Publications, London.

Matrix (1984) *Women and the Man Made Environment*, Pluto Press, London.

McCafferty, P. (1994) *Living Independently: A Study of the Housing Needs of Elderly and Disabled People*, HMSO, London.

Morris, J. and Winn, M. (1990) *Housing and Social Inequality*, Hilary Shipman, London.

National Federation of Housing Associations (1993) *Accommodating Diversity: The Design of Housing for Minority Ethnic, Religious and Cultural Groups*, North Housing Trust, Newcastle upon Tyne.

Oakley, A. (1974) *Housewife*, Penguin, Harmandsworth.

Office for National Statistics (1996) *Social Trends 26*, 1996 Edition, HMSO, London.

Office for National Statistics (1997) *Social Trends 27*, 1997 Edition, HMSO, London.

OPCS(1993a) *1991 Census, Household Composition, Great Britain*, Government Statistical Service, OPCS and General Register Office of Scotland, HMSO, London.

OPCS(1993b) *1991 Census, Communal Establishments, Great Britain*, Vol. 1 of 2, Government Statistical Service, OPCS and General Register Office Scotland, HMSO, London.

OPCS (1993c) *1991 Census, Persons Aged 60 and Over, Great Britain*, Government Statistical Service. OPCS and General Register Office Scotland, HMSO, London.

Peace, S., Kellaher, L. and Willcocks, D. (1997) *Re-evaluating Residental Care*, Open University Press, Buckingham.

Philipson, C. (1990) *Delivering Community Care Services for Older People: Problems and Prospects*, Centre for Social Gerontology, Keele University, Stoke on Trent.

Randell, B. (1995) *Staying Put – The Best Move I'll Ever Make*, Anchor Housing Association, Oxford.

Rooney, R., Lewis, B. and Schüle, R. (1989) *Home is Where the Heart Is*, Yorkshire Arts Circus in association with Continuum, West Yorkshire.

Scher, P. (1994) 'Learning by experience', *Hospital Development*, September.

Shelter (1994) *Homelessness: What's the problem?*, Shelter, London.

Wickings, I. (1994) *Improving Hospital Design*, King Edward's Hospital Fund for London.

Women's Design Service (WDS) (1991) *Women Who Work: Report on a Survey of Whipps Cross Hospital Antenatal Clinic Waiting Area*, Women's Design Service, London.

Women's Design Service (WDS) (1993) *Antenatal Waiting Areas Broadsheet*, Women's Design Service, London.

Acknowledgements

Grateful acknowledgement is made to the following sources for
permission to reproduce material in this unit:

Text

p. 21: 'A Lifetime House', in *Foundations,* Feb. 1997, Joseph Rowntree
Foundation; *p. 36:* Haskey J. 'Population review: Families and
households in Great Britian', in *Population Trends,* No. 85, Autumn 1996,
Office for National Statistics, HMSO, crown copyright is reproduced
with the permission of the Controller of Her Majesty's Stationery Office.

Figures

Figure 3: Figure 10.1 from *Social Trends,* 27, 1997, p.169, Office for
National Statistics, HMSO, crown copyright is reproduced with the
permission of the Controller of Her Majesty's Stationery Office.

Tables

Table 1: Haskey J. 'Population review: Families and households in Great
Britian', in *Population Trends*; No. 85, Autumn 1996, Office for National
Statistics, HMSO, crown copyright is reproduced with the permission of
the Controller of Her Majesty's Stationery Office.

Illustrations

P. 8: all Sally and Richard Greenhill; *p. 11:* Joanne O'Brien/Format; *p. 17:*
Age Concern, England, photo: Andrew Wiard, model: Gloria Williams;
p. 18: Suzanne Roden/Format; *p. 21:* courtesy of the Joseph Rowntree
Foundation; *p. 26:* Sally and Richard Greenhill; *p. 28:* Women's Design
Service, Sue Cavanagh; *p. 44:* Brenda Price/Format.

Unit 7
Interaction with Care Environments

Prepared for the course team by Sheila Peace

While you are working on Unit 7, you will need:
- Course Reader
- *The Good Study Guide*
- Audio Cassette 2, side 1
- Media Notes
- Care in the UK

Contents

Introduction

In Unit 6 you looked at some of the issues concerning the physical environments in which care takes place, and began to consider the relationship between accommodation and care. Unit 7 takes this a stage further looking at two major issues which link people and places. First, there is the concept of space and how it is used in care environments. For people who live in group settings maintaining some kind of privacy is important, and this often means having a space in which to be themselves. Issues of access to different spaces also become important as does who has rights over spaces and why? Interaction within care environments can be considered at the level of the group and the individual. We began to explore some of these themes around personal space in Unit 4 and they are developed here.

The second theme for this unit is attachment to place. Places often mean something to us, they say something about ourselves and the people who are important to us. Many people receiving care stress the importance of remaining in their own home and yet moving between different places to receive care is common. Attachment to home has to be set alongside attachment to people, and coping with transitions between places, moving in and out of care settings, can be disrupting.

To help explore these ideas you will be hearing more from Esther Hurdle, who you met in Unit 6, and also from Alan and Pauline Bright, an older couple living in their own home. Alan has Alzheimer's disease and he and his wife are supported by a number of community health and social services as well as a day centre service. You'll be hearing from some of these workers as well.

The core questions for this unit are:

Core questions

- How is space defined in care settings?
- Why is privacy important?
- Who has access to different types of spaces in care settings?
- What meanings are attached to places and how are they important to well-being?
- How do people cope with moving between different care environments?

Section 1
Place, space and access

Looking at the physical environment leads to a consideration of space. In Unit 6 you began to consider the design of the domestic home as an environment for care. The design of buildings shapes different spaces, distinguishing the functions of places such as domestic housing, public parks or office space. In this unit the focus is on spaces in which care takes place – a wide variety of ordinary housing, day centres, hospitals, hostels and homes. But why be interested in space in a course about health and social care? What is important for care is how people use space and how it affects the relationships between them. It is part of what we call the social environment.

1.1   Defining space

Defining space is difficult, after all it's just there, isn't it? It surrounds us. It's common when we think of space to think of space travel. Here we stay firmly on the ground. What helps us to put boundaries around space, and define it in different ways, is the way in which people use it and have access to it.

Public space, private space?

Activity 1   **Different kinds of space**

Allow a few minutes   Stop and think about the place you are in as you read this workbook. How would you describe it? Would you say it was a public space which anyone could enter, or a private space where you can be on your own?

Comment   If you are sitting in a public library then it's easy to see this as a public space which everyone has access to. Even so you may be sitting in the reference section of the library which has certain rules about keeping quiet and not disturbing other people, so even here certain people may be excluded. If you are at home, then you might say that you are in a private space but just how private may depend on other people and what they are doing. To outsiders the home may be a private place but just where you are in the home and who might disturb you may make it more or less public or private. If you live with other people the kitchen can be a far more public space than a study, for instance in terms of whether or not you are likely to be left alone.

This activity has made a distinction between public and private space on the basis of who has access and the activity being undertaken. When someone is studying there is often an expectation that they need peace and quiet, although this may be hard to find.

Expectations, customs and practices surrounding activities often influence how space is defined and become reinforced through the design of buildings. As we saw in Unit 6, the physical environment of domestic housing has been designed in ways which often reinforce ideas about domestic activities, roles within the family, and where they should take place. Some ideas over how we use space change over time; others, it seems, remain fixed. Before returning to issues of public and private space, here are some other factors which might influence how space is used in the home.

Activity 2   Young people's views on the use of space
in the home

Allow about 10 minutes   These comments by three young people living in Calderdale were recorded in 1989 as part of an oral history project. Read the comments and consider how the following factors influence ideas about and use of space in the home:

(a)   past experience

(b)   changes in lifestyle

(c)   importance of privacy

(d)   traditional ideas about behaviour.

> *When my parents' generation came over we were in what you might call the houses of desperation, overcrowded housing. Sometimes people would work on day shifts and then swap beds with night shift workers. It was a difficult environment to cope with. We want more, are more individualistic. My bedroom, for instance, is covered with posters of people like Madonna and Michael Jackson, whereas the living room only has pictures of mosques and religious things on the walls.*
> *(Asian female)*

> *I'm content to stay with my parents. I've got my own room and I can do what I want with it as far as decoration goes. A job is my first priority. I've been out of work since I left school. Then I might consider trying to buy my own place. A scaled down model of my parents' house with a bit of a garden would do to start with.*
> *(Male)*

> *We have got a through-lounge, two rooms knocked through, so we're getting the use of the room and there's no waste of space. We don't need a dining room since our meal times are different and we only sit down together for Saturday tea and Sunday lunch. Having space is important. My parent's*

A room of your own

living room was very small. The other room was the kitchen. When my husband and I lived with them, we had no privacy and it was unthinkable for us to go up to our room. We would all get on top of each other sometimes, especially once there was a baby. (Female)

(Rooney et al., 1989)

Comment   I noted the following:

(a) **The influence of their own and other family members' experiences of sharing space**. Experiences influence attitudes and behaviour – in the last example, space and privacy are important to this young woman now her family has a home of their own. She feels this way as a result of having had to share with one set of parents. I wonder if older people who move in with their children and share their space feel the same way? The way people use space within the home can also relate to wider factors – the young Asian woman comments on the way her family worked in shifts when they first arrived in this country. The older generation within this household had little choice but to put up with overcrowding, they had little opportunity for privacy.

(b) **Changes in lifestyle affecting use of space within the home**. How space is used in the home can also be related to different activities. Again, the couple don't feel the need for a dining room because they don't eat together all the time, so they have created more open space. They feel that 'there's no waste of space'. So there are issues here about the changing nature of work, childcare and leisure interests for men and women and how the home is used.

(c) **The importance of private space over which you have control**. The second young person interviewed has decided to remain at home with his parents. For him 'finding a job' is more important than moving out, but that feels all right because he has a room of his own and has some control over what it looks like. So having some private space and being able to personalise it is important. We'll come back to this point later in the unit.

(d) **The influence of what are thought to be appropriate and inappropriate activities and behaviours for different types of**

space. While in the UK the family home may be seen as a private place, within the home there are spaces which are more public (living/dining rooms) or more private (bedrooms/bathrooms), and people of different generations and different ages may think about these spaces in different ways. For example – the last quote comments on living as a married couple in their parents' house 'it was unthinkable for us to go up to our room'. Bedroom spaces, when used by couples in their parents' houses, may not be seen as the appropriate place to retreat to by the older generation. This reflects attitudes held about intimacy and sexual behaviour, but it does mean that bedroom space can be under-utilised and privacy can be withheld. Attitudes to the use of space are also held about children of different sexes having rooms of their own, whereas it is all right for children of the same sex to share.

Different cultural and religious practices can also affect the use of space. Such diversity can be incorporated into the design of accommodation but it also affects the use of space, for example in some groups separation of men's and women's space in the home is the norm:

> There are many degrees of such separation. In a number of Muslim households, women do not enter the men's space when guests are present. In strict Orthodox Jewish households women and men will not socialise together or take part together in religious observance. In many households of other cultures, such as Hindu, Rastafarian and Sikh, the tendency is for men and women to socialise separately.
>
> (National Federation of Housing Associations, 1993, p. 16)

Perhaps the views of the young people from Calderdale are not unexpected given that they are either yet to leave home or are starting their own family. But they begin to tell us something about the importance of privacy and how the use of space relates to attitudes and behaviours which may be influenced by age, gender, social class, generation, family history, and cultural and religious traditions.

These statements were made about familiar environments which the interviewees knew well. For people living in care settings the unwritten rules about how space is used may be less obvious, if no less complex. Attitudes may be determined by other people or the needs of the organisation.

Key points

- Public and private space can be defined on the basis of who has access to space and the activity being undertaken within it.

- There are many influences on how space is used within the home. Traditional views on the roles of men and women and the nature of domestic activities are important. Other influences are generational, class, cultural and religious differences, as well as those related to changing lifestyles.

- An understanding of privacy is important to how space is used.

1.2 Privacy and the nature of public and private space

Privacy as a way of maintaining aspects of self-identity has emerged as an important subject in discussions about the design and organisation of residential care settings. In the main when people talk about privacy in this context they are talking about people's need for a private space in which they can be themselves. In this section we concentrate on issues of privacy and access as they relate to:

*   physical space, and
*   personal space.

Activity 3

Allow about 20 minutes

Public space, private space and a need for privacy

Central to this activity is the extract from Willcocks *et al.* (1987) which is Chapter 10 in the Reader. This reports on findings from a national consumer study of local authority residential care homes for older people that was carried out in 1980/81. It was the first study of its kind to ask older residents themselves about the physical environments in which they lived. The researchers talked to 1,000 residents and 400 members of staff living in 100 homes as well as carrying out detailed qualitative research in four care homes. Many of the buildings were typical of purpose-built homes run by local authorities in the post-war period.

Read to the end of the section entitled 'Autonomy' and as you read try to answer the following questions:

(a)   What spaces do the authors see as public and private spaces?

(b)   How do they suggest that the arrangement of these spaces may affect people's behaviour?

(c)   How do the authors define privacy?

(d)   How might an institutional environment prevent people from finding privacy?

Comment

(a)   The authors consider lounges, dining rooms and circulation spaces which link areas, as public spaces. They see bedrooms, bathrooms and WCs as private spaces. They don't mention office space but this is also found in residential homes and is often the private space of administrative and senior staff who allow other people access.

(b)   Different designs of homes are described and these are said to be more or less integrated in terms of how public and private space is arranged. By integration they mean the arrangement of space and whether public and private areas are near to, or far from each other. It is suggested that where some public and private spaces are closer together they encourage activities.

(c)   In Chapter 10 privacy is talked about in a number of different ways:
        solitude – separation from other people
        anonymity – being within a group but apart from it
        and they also mention the relationship between **intimacy** and **privacy**.

(d)   In relation to these homes studied in 1980/81, the authors comment on various ways in which achieving privacy may be difficult for residents. The lack of single rooms as a private space into which people could retreat was a major obstacle, 'only half of all the residents in the 100 homes had a bedroom of their own'.

Residents in the study could not lock their rooms either to protect their possessions or to control their own space. The authors comment 'without such control this private space becomes common territory', more easily a public space. The public and communal nature of lounges and dining rooms, coupled with the lack of private spaces within these homes led to visiting taking place in public areas. So there was little opportunity for private times with friends and relatives.

The design and use of space in care settings can have a strong influence on everyday experience. This research showed that the maintenance of personal autonomy or control was severely hampered by poor resources. People were more likely to make their rooms their own if they had a room to themselves and it was larger rather than smaller. It is more common today for residents to have a single room and in a way this has become a symbol of the degree to which privacy has begun to be acknowledged.

Where public and private space is very separate then the need for staff to be accountable for residents' activities may mean that residents spend a lot of their day time in public spaces so that they can be seen easily. Anonymity is often maintained in public areas by the territorial protection of chairs, the 'backs to the wall' arrangements and behaviour based on avoidance of eye contact to maintain a distance. Chairs can also be protected as private space within a public place as this quote from a study of an American nursing home shows.

> On the grounds and in the lobby of Murray Manor there are no official private places, but residents do maintain 'their chairs' at certain times of the day. Everyone knows, for example, that Cora Mommsen sits in the south-west chair in the side lobby during the early afternoon, reading her 'stories'. If someone else is seated there when she appears, another resident is likely to say to the one seated, 'That's Cora's chair,' or the occupant may say 'Oops! Am I in your chair, Cora?' Such talk signifies a private place and sustains Cora's assumption that she can 'act in private'.
>
> (Gubrium, 1975, p. 37)

The public lounge

Ittelson *et al.* have defined privacy as:

> *... the freedom of individuals to choose what they will communicate about themselves and to whom they will communicate in a particular situation.*
>
> *(1974, p. 152)*

The conditions and circumstances in which this 'freedom to choose' takes place can vary enormously, and 'a particular situation' may not be dependent on place and space at all. However as we have just seen, certain contexts can make the availability of privacy more or less possible.

Privacy in residential homes

In a recent guide to standards in residential care homes the following were seen as indicators of 'processes likely to achieve good outcomes' in relation to privacy:

- staff, visitors and other service users appreciate the differences between private and public space

- service users are able to lock their own rooms for which risks have been assessed and agreed

- service users exercise freedom to be left alone in their own rooms

- staff, visitors and other service users respect the right to privacy

- service users have access to a telephone they can use without being overheard.

(Residential Forum, 1996, p. 29)

Establishing and maintaining privacy depends on how people behave towards each other and it can be supported by design and access to private space.

Key points

- Privacy concerns the freedom of individuals to choose what they will communicate about themselves and to whom. It can take various forms and be influenced by place.

- In care settings privacy is often related to the need for people to have private space over which they have control.

- People can behave in certain ways to create their own private space within public places.

- Group settings like residential homes may offer residents more or less access to private space.

1.3 Access to physical space

Looking at privacy and space introduces issues of access. Control over access to public and private spaces tells us a lot about how people guard their privacy. Most physical spaces have *boundaries* that can be seen – marked by doors, walls, dividers, lines on the floor or changes in colour schemes. Some of these physical boundaries can be secured by locking, which can give a greater sense of control to either the cared for or the carer. But boundaries may also be psychological, for example if you share a bedroom with someone how do you divide up the space? Much will depend on the level of intimacy between you but even so, it is common to divide the space in your mind and reinforce this with physical objects.

Caring relationships often demand that people allow other people access into their space. They may invade not only physical space but in many cases also personal space around their body. In Unit 3, Section 2 we talked about the distance which carers and cared for set up between themselves as a boundary. Here we continue the theme of boundaries in relation to space.

Activity 4 **Privacy and access**

Allow about 10 minutes Think about where you live and the boundaries that exist around and within it. Note down:

- all the places where you could go to find solitude or be on your own. Is there anywhere you can lock the door?

- any places where you don't have free access, e.g. where you'd have to knock to be allowed in.

If you live with other people consider whether the answers to these points would be different for other members of your household.

Now think about people who come in and out of your home. Who has free access, who has to be invited in?

If it helps, draw a quick floor plan and write your answers on the plan.

Comment I can't tell what you came up with but I thought about this activity in relation to my family home which is a ground floor flat in an old Edwardian semi-detached house in London. Looking at the private space of the flat in terms of access and privacy for me seemed to be determined by role and age. As a mother of two children, I found it very difficult to say that anywhere really affords 'somewhere to be on my own' until they are asleep. So my privacy combines space with time – I can find it late at night. A colleague who lives on her own also commented on the way time and space combine. She said that although she values her privacy she does wonder sometimes what would happen if she had an accident and could not raise help.

In thinking about access, the only internal room with a lock on the door is the bathroom – and this also contains the loo – but as the children are fairly young, I often leave the door unlocked so that I am accessible. But that is not the case for all members of the family. My husband always locks the bathroom door and my 10 year old son has just put a sign on his bedroom door telling everyone who does not support the 'Arsenal' to keep out. However, while I now have to ask to go into his room, and often forget, he still does not have a key to the front door so his overall access to the flat is restricted. Only the adult family members have free access to this door. Again this tells us something about the influence on access of gender, age and the roles and relationships between people.

When you thought about who you allow into your home, you might have considered the meter readers or the plumber who comes to fix the washing machine. While the electricity or gas people have a legal right of entry to read the meters, the plumber has come to do a repair and is therefore invited into your home to carry out a service. You may ask to see some identification before you, or someone delegated by you, lets them in. To this extent you are in control of their access.

The places we live in are usually *defensible* spaces, in other words we can decide who comes in and out. Some *territorial boundaries* can be based on legal title, so there is a sense of ownership – but ownership doesn't always guarantee privacy or security. What about burglars? They are uninvited, invade your space, may take your possessions, and it is common for people who have lost property to feel insecure, a victim, as if they themselves have been threatened. They have lost a sense of control. At a much less dramatic level we can also think of having guests to stay – invited of course, but when we say 'make yourself at home' do we mean sit in the bath for hours? Yet again we have unspoken limits. So territorial control doesn't always mean that you have control over access.

This activity shows that different people may have more or less control over space. Within situations where care is given and received the nature of this control can have important implications for people's lives. Here we look at the following issues around access and care in the domestic home and in care settings:

• access and control

• access and accountability

• access and surveillance.

Access and control

Activity 5	Controlling access, crossing boundaries

Allow about 15 minutes   Return to Audio Cassette 2, side 1. In Unit 6, you listened to the first half of the interview with Esther Hurdle. Now listen to the rest. Here Esther talks about her relationship with her four home carers and compares life in the hospital with life at home.

As you listen try and note down:

(a)   what boundaries the home carers may be crossing

(b)   where Esther gains a greater sense of control – at home or in hospital? Why is this?

Comment   (a)   Esther's four home carers often let themselves into the house and therefore have privileged access to the private space of her and her family. They also have access to Esther herself and her own personal space. However, Esther's comments give us a very strong sense of her control over her new home and how she feels this gives her certain rights. One of these rights is over who comes into her home

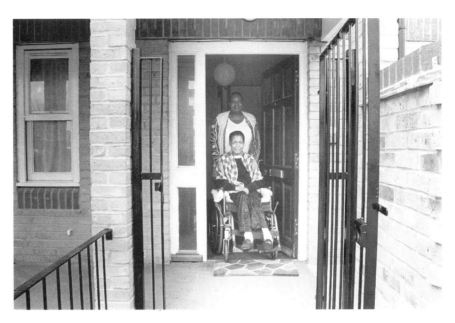

Crossing boundaries

and what they do. She values the fact that she now has the continuity of the same people coming in.

When she left hospital, her first home carer obviously tried to do everything for her, and Esther felt that she was more concerned with her own needs as a worker.

She knew I could do that sort of thing and yet she insisted on doing it and I didn't feel it was her right to say I'm paid to do this so let me just get on with it. I think she was just doing it because she just wanted to rush herself to get out. Take time to get to know the person and let them tell you what they are needing.

This home carer does not seem to have considered Esther's needs or the boundaries she was crossing.

(b)   When Esther talks about life in hospital she talks about it as a place where there is little or no privacy; where she was constantly accessible and yet where her needs depended on other people's routines. In contrast, within her own home she can 'just go to my room and shut the door and just forget about everything. ... 'You're on your own, you've got your own privacy there'. The way she says this tells us just how important it is to her.

Her comments about members of her family are interesting. She doesn't always feel in control of them. This tells us something about the difference in care relationships which involve members of the family and those which involve paid carers. After all, it is their home as well, they have their own routines and needs to attend to.

You will probably recognise that many of Esther's comments are similar to those of the disabled women interviewed in the Reader chapter by Morris which you read in Unit 3. Esther's story also tells us about the way ownership of place and space can influence the control those receiving care have over when and how care is given. Here the sense of control felt by being at home is seen to convey rights over access to space which can be both physical and personal. However for other people on the receiving end of care work being in control may be less easy. For example, in an ongoing study of the interaction between community nurses, older people and their carers, Buckeldee (1996) demonstrates the relative freedom with which nurses access people's houses and fill someone else's space with their equipment and medication.

Also if you think about the care practice in Cedar Court nursing home which you read about in Unit 4, you will recall how the use of public and private spaces within that home reinforced the control staff had over residents. There we talked about control in Goffman's terms as front and back stage work. Here we can see how these realities can be reinforced in spatial terms. We will be coming back to this chapter in Unit 8.

Access and accountability

Another interesting example of the use of space and access in relation to care within the family home is seen in childminding. Here children who, as we saw in Unit 6, are not members of the household, may occupy a family home for long periods of the day. Their access to space in the home is controlled by the childminder. However, this home is also a care setting and as such it is registered with and inspected by the local authority on an annual basis. Inspectors therefore have access to the home in order to assess both the quality of care provided and the environment in which it takes place. We will be looking at the regulation of care settings in Unit 8. Here the issues are: access to the physical environment, control and accountability.

Activity 6   ## Whose territory?

Allow about 10 minutes

The box below contains an extract from an interview with Maureen, the childminder you met in Unit 6. Here she is talking about the way the children she looks after, their parents and her own family use the space in her house. She also talks about the annual inspection process.

Read through the interview and try to answer these questions.

(a)   Does it appear that different people have different access to space in the house?

(b)   What might influence Maureen's views on the way space is used and boundaries crossed?

(c)   What is the main reason for the modifications made to this environment? How have Maureen and her family reconciled these different issues of access and accountability?

At the beginning of the interview she is talking about the ground floor of her house. She is sitting with the interviewer in the front room which is seen as the best room for receiving visitors.

Maureen

Int. So what you've done down here is you've kept this room as a room for your family but you've more or less given up the room behind it haven't you?

M. Yes, you have to sit in the front room but saying that all the children use it, they all use it all the time. I don't lock the door and say you can't use that room. They use the whole house from top to bottom through the day. They use the whole house just as if they were my own children and there's use of the back room as a toy room for them and I've had a lot of work done in the garden ...

Int. Do you think that other members of your household have enough privacy — you know, if they want to be on their own?

M. Oh yes, 'cause Tracey has her own bedroom, and Derek, my eldest son, had his and when he moved Aidan took it over ... The way I feel it's as though I've got lots of families you know what I mean having all the children. ... Some of the time they [the parents] just want to come in get their children and they like to go, I don't like that. I like them to come in and have a chat with me and have a cup of tea.

Int. So your front door is open most of the time?

M. That's right.

Int. And the parents just walk in and out. Does that bother you?

M. No it doesn't bother me at all, I love people coming into the house and I like people to come in and make themselves at home. I like to be friendly to people ... that's my nature you know, it suits me all over, and I love the house full of people. I don't like it when there's nobody about you know. I like to have people in the house all day 'cause the day passes quicker.

Int. Was it like that in your family home?

M. It was yes, my mother's door was always open and anybody was always welcome to walk in and help themselves to tea and coffee and whatever they wanted. My mother was like that all her life, her mother was like that you know, and people says nowadays why don't you keep your door locked, you know, but well my door is locked ... during [part of] the day. If you come during the day I put the lock on the door, you'd have to knock loud cause there's so many things happening nowadays, you know what I mean.

Int. How often does the day care officer come to inspect your home?

M. Once a year, they let me know when they are coming.

Int. Would you mind if they just turned up unannounced?

M. No.

Int. And what kinds of things have you had to do to your home because you are a childminder?

M. Well, I had to get a new cooker guard, a fire blanket and put safety catches on the cupboards. I had to have special wire meshed glass put in the french windows to the height of the children in case they fell through it. And there are window locks throughout the house in case the children opened the bottom of the windows and fell out. I don't need a stairgate as I don't have any very young children now, but when I have a baby I've had to change the bedrooms upstairs to accommodate a cot. Also, I have a first aid kit on hand all the time and all bleaches etc. have to be put out of reach.

In the garden I had to put a fence around the fishpond and at the side of the house I had to put up a shed for buckets and brushes – so there have been quite a lot of things.

Int. Do you mind having to do that?

M. No, not at all, it's for a good cause. My daycare officer says you are doing the childminding, so you are responsible, it's different for the parents in their own home, it's up to them what they do.

Comment   These were my thoughts on reading through the interview and trying to answer the questions.

(a)   Maureen appears to let the children in her care have a very free rein over different parts of her house. This is very much in keeping with her view that while the children are in her house they are part of her family. While she doesn't bar them from going into the front room there is an expectation that this is a sitting room, somewhere for her family to go away from the children. In contrast she has turned another room on the ground floor of the house into a playroom. The children are also allowed upstairs but she does exert some control over where they go and, as she says, if her own children want some privacy then they can go to their rooms.

Whose territory?

(b)   I felt that much of Maureen's attitude to how space is used stems from her own childhood, (she was brought up in a rural part of Northern Ireland). She obviously likes to have people around and dislikes parents who won't stop for a chat. So there is much coming and going to and from the house, though this openness is also tempered by some concern about security. The front door is now unlikely to be open all day.

(c)   The modifications that have been made to the house are all concerned with safety, fire safety in the main but also concerns over children hurting themselves physically through smashing glass or having an accident in the garden. She does not seem to find these modifications intrusive, rather she sees that her responsibility for other people's children is different from their parents.

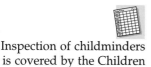

Inspection of childminders is covered by the Children Act, 1989.

Whilst Maureen likes people to have access to her home, she still retains control over it. She could decide that the children and adults who are not family members can only have very limited access to certain parts of her home but she couldn't refuse access to the inspectors doing their annual inspection.

This activity shows us that care activities undertaken in the privacy of the home also have to be accountable and open to scrutiny.

Access and surveillance

The third issue relating to access concerns surveillance – that part of care work that is concerned with 'watching over' someone. Again this is related to safety, risk-taking and a recognition that carers, whether formal or informal, have responsibilities for which they can be accountable. The following two activities are concerned with the way in which the design of non-domestic care settings can facilitate or hinder watching, how this relates to rights of access, and what this means for the experience of those being cared for.

Activity 7   Negotiating care environments

Allow about 20 minutes

Go back to Chapter 10 in the Reader and read the remaining sections beginning at 'Negotiability'. Here the authors consider how the behaviour of older people in care homes can be influenced by issues concerning rights of access, orientation, ease of mobility and issues of safety. Read each of these four sections and at the end of each try and note down one or two key points.

Comment   The following are some of the key points raised in the reading.

Rights of access
- In residential homes residents may not have access to all areas of the building such as kitchens, laundries and staff rooms. This can mean that they lose access to everyday tasks.
- Staff have rights of access to all routes around the building which the authors say is 'a consequence of their duty to care for and watch over residents'.

Orientation
- If people cannot understand the layout of a building they may find they have to rely on other people more than they need to.
- There are ways of making buildings easier to negotiate such as colour coding and signs.

Ease of mobility
- Access can be impeded by an environment which has not been designed to meet the needs of the user group.
- The arrangement of public and private space can hinder access and this may be reinforced by the way the organisation operates.

Safety
- The safety of residents is a key concern of staff. It is related to risk-taking and concerns over responsibility.
- A major task for the staff in this study was surveillance, watching residents.
- Concerns with safety are reinforced by the physical environment, e.g. fire doors and alarm systems.

This reading highlights some of the issues around access within formal care settings which revolve around the different needs of those who give and those who receive care. In environmental terms the building is both a living and working environment, and tensions exist over access and over issues of responsibility and risk-taking. These issues may be even more pronounced within the hospital environment. The quote by Twigg in Section 1 of Unit 3 comments on this very point.

> *The public nature of the space relates to the access of professionals, of non-kin, non friends – of relationships that have no private quality to them ...*
> *(Twigg, 1997, p. 228)*

Activity 8   **Access and surveillance**

Allow about 10 minutes   Imagine you are a patient on a general medical ward. The layout of this ward is shown in Figure 1. There are four four-bedded bays, two for men and two for women, and a linking corridor off which there are bathrooms and toilets plus a nurses' station and other treatment rooms. The doors to the main corridor of the hospital are controlled by a security system which only allows visitors free access at visiting times. You are recovering from an operation, are mobile and able to walk to the bathroom. Think about the spaces marked on this plan, including the corridor outside the ward doors, and then decide:

(a)   whether they are public or private spaces, and what might make them more or less public/private

(b)   who has access to these spaces, and

(c)   who controls the access and why.

Make some notes.

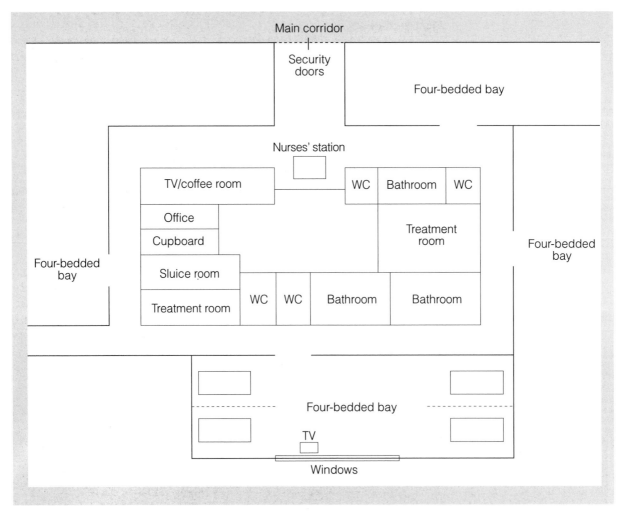

Figure 1
Access and surveillance

Comment   How did you get on? If you have been a hospital patient then you probably used that experience to think through the activity. You may have come up with some of the following points:

(a)   It's quite difficult to make the distinction between public and private space. Everything beyond the main doors to the corridor could be public. But then within the ward life is also very public – nurses, doctors, auxiliaries and other patients have access to all parts of the ward. Bathrooms and toilets should be private spaces and lockable, though of course you may need assistance.

There are usually curtains that can be pulled around hospital beds so you could create a private space. You might do this if you needed a bedpan or if a member of the family wanted a private chat – although it is probable that you can still be heard if not seen. But if you just wanted to get away from the other people on the ward you might feel a bit awkward about drawing the curtains. The nurses like to be able to see people and they might think something was wrong. It is not seen as appropriate behaviour for a patient to be always creating their own private space. I remember my mother using a personal stereo during a hospital stay a few years ago. She often listened to music with her eyes shut to help her through what felt like a great ordeal. However, the nurses were more than a little irritated that she had decided to cut herself off from everyone else in this way.

(b) The staff have most access over space on the ward. As a mobile patient you would have free access to the bathroom and WC, however you may not be able to take a bath on your own. You might walk backwards and forwards to the tea/coffee room, but as this is a mixed ward you might feel that your access is restricted by the presence of members of the opposite sex and that you want to stay within your own bay.

(c) Control over access is weighted towards staff by the nature of their work. They need to be able to observe people given their responsibility for patient well-being. The siting of the nurses' station in this layout and the entry system gives staff control over who enters the ward area. This is an issue of security which also relates to responsibility. However, the bay design does not allow observation of patients from the nurses' station.

Different people may have different levels of control over access to a ward like this. For example, visitors may have their access restricted to certain times of day. However, if a consultant was doing a ward round then the use of space would change. Access to individuals may become more controlled by the medical team but private space would be created for consultation. This would be seen as more legitimate than the patient creating private space for themselves. Once the medical team had disappeared then the nurses' work of watching would take over again.

Control may also be exerted by one group of patients over another. Issues have been raised about mixed wards and the Patients' Association has called for their abolition following complaints over privacy. One woman reported her experience of a mixed ward:

> By evening, the atmosphere on the ward was like a saloon bar or a men's hostel. Male patients were wandering about without their dressing gowns, some in their underwear. They were using the gents next to my room, fastening their clothes as they came out.

(Patients' Association, 1996)

The hospital ward portrayed here is quite modern in that there are only four beds in each bay. This is very different from the old 'Nightingale' wards with their rows of beds facing each other and a central nurses station. These still exist, of course. An NHS hospital is quite a public setting unless something very personal is happening to you, and even then it can be quite difficult to maintain privacy. If you are a private patient and have paid for your care then most probably you will have a room to yourself. Here privacy will be easier to maintain but for some people being on their own can lead to isolation.

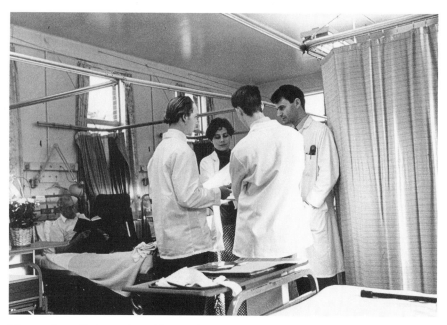

The ward as a living and working environment

Key points

• Access to space can be related to both design and organisation.

• Access to space can be determined by time.

• Access can be dependent on who has most control over space – this may relate to age, gender, role, activity.

• Access to space can relate to issues of responsibility and accountability.

1.4 Personal space

> Some thirty inches from my nose
> The frontier of my Person goes
> And all the untilled air between
> Is private *pagus* or *demesne*
> Stranger, unless with bedroom eyes
> I beckon you to fraternize,
> Beware of rudely crossing it:
> I have no gun, but I can spit
>
> (W.H. Auden, 'Some thirty inches from my nose')

While privacy may involve a physical space in which you have control over access, place may be secondary to the purpose of privacy. Chapter 10 in the Reader defined privacy in terms of *solitude, intimacy* and *anonymity.* Westin (1967) added a fourth state of privacy – *reserve*, to identify the need for people to be able to withhold information about themselves. As we saw in Unit 4, care relationships can involve touching and nakedness, and finding ways of managing feelings about intimacy. Such experiences have a spatial element which involves negotiating boundaries that are personal and psychological. It involves our own *personal space*, or what has been called that 'protective bubble' we carry around ourselves.

Whose space is it anyway?

The sociologist George Simmel described this concept in the early 1900s and it has received attention from other disciplines, psychologists and anthropologists (Hall, 1966; Sommer, 1969). The ideas propose that you can distinguish distances around the body where people experience different actions with more or less comfort. For example think about standing in a queue where you don't know anyone. Most people keep two or three feet between themselves and people in front of them; if someone pushes from behind then everyone feels uncomfortable. We can sense other people as close or distant but how we do this is based on lots of different reactions – to tone of voice, whether we can see them, the distance they are from us, their stance, the context in which the interaction is taking place, and most importantly how well we know them and in what way. These reactions can also depend on cultural traditions and customs about intimacy which, as the work of Jourard highlighted in Unit 4, also relate to gender. The French may kiss each other on the cheek as an everyday greeting but the British may feel uncomfortable with this degree of public affection.

There are lots of provisos to be made about how different individuals experience personal space but you probably agree that it does exist. Let's think about it in a bit more detail.

First, personal space does not extend equally in all directions around the body. So we feel less invaded by someone else when they stand alongside us than when they stand in front or behind us. Think about the hairdressers: it is quite common in this country to sit with someone standing very closely behind you but this feels OK because there is mirror in front of you and you can see where they are. If you couldn't see them you wouldn't feel so secure. Of course, you also know what is going to happen to you at the hairdressers – well, usually.

Second, there is a distance at which people feel comfortable having others near them. Of course, in an intimate embrace with someone very dear distance may be the last consideration. But most of the time people observe the unwritten rules about distance. Unless of course we find ourselves crushed together on a bus or in a train when people commonly switch off, pretend everyone is really a non-person, and gaze at their feet.

Third, control over who is and who is not allowed within personal space can vary in terms of situation, circumstance and appropriateness of behaviour given a particular culture.

Fourth, mobility is very important – if it is possible to move out of a situation where an invasion of personal space occurs then that's fine, but if someone can't move quickly or easily, then other people may have an advantage. This may be an important issue for people with physical impairments which impede mobility.

Unit 4 considered how care workers 'established a logical framework' (see Unit 4, Section 3.2 'Meanings of touching') for coping with intimate care – here a spatial dimension is added to the relationship. The next activity considers how one care worker, June Blakeway, deals with issues of physical and personal space as part of her work.

Activity 9   **'It's more "hands on"'**

Allow about 15 minutes

Listen to the first part of section 2 of Audio Cassette 2, side 1. June Blakeway is a home carer working in Bletchley. Here June is talking about her work and how she feels about working in other people's houses and giving personal care. Stop the tape at the point where June comments 'it makes them more comfortable', before the narrator introduces Mr Bright. Alan Bright, who features later on in this unit, is one of June's clients. You will be starting the tape again here in Activity 14.

As you listen to June talking try to do the following:

(a)   think about how often she goes in and out of other people's homes

(b)   make a list of the all the tasks which June performs and then note down which tasks involve June in crossing boundaries of (i) physical space and (ii) personal space

(c)   record how June feels about carrying out these tasks

(d)   note down what she says is important when carrying out personal care of an intimate nature.

You might like to listen to this section of the tape twice.

Comment   (a)   Listening to June talking I was a bit overwhelmed by all the people that one home carer could see in a day and all the tasks she undertook. Fifteen people seen in an evening, 20 in a morning and evening. This means going in and out of other people's houses on a daily basis and yet listening to June I thought that she felt it was very important to maintain some distance between herself and her clients.

(b)   I came up with the following tasks:

shower and shave – personal, physical
getting dressed – personal, physical
getting breakfast – physical
making beds – physical
housework – physical
shopping – physical
getting undressed – personal, physical
bathing – personal, physical
putting to bed – personal, physical.

With the exception of shopping, all of these tasks happen in the home and many involve personal care and crossing the boundaries of an individual's or family's physical and personal space.

(c)   June is very conscious that she should not 'intrude' – she says 'I'm not there to intrude at all', and she doesn't feel happy 'opening someone else's cupboard doors'. In this sense she is not taking control of someone else's space, she observes rules about behaviour in someone else's house.

(d)   This carries through to her feelings about intimate care. Here the important thing is to maintain the individual's modesty and dignity. She reinforces this by saying:

> *You would never leave somebody completely naked or if they were having a shower you would keep the nakedness for the minimum amount of time. You would drape them with something as soon as possible just to keep their dignity really – it makes them more comfortable.*

The issues raised by listening to June reinforce the discussions we had in Unit 4 and link directly to the ideas put forward by Twigg in Chapter 30 of the Reader. What we have been doing here is stressing the way in which people use space and how both the physical environment and the relationships between people affect access. The rest of this unit is concerned with what places mean to us.

Key points

- Everyone can define their own personal space. How people react to invasions of personal space can depend on a range of factors – including age, gender, social class, cultural and religious custom and traditions, and situation.

- In care relationships those giving care should be conscious of the power they may have over the physical and personal space of the cared for.

Study skills: A personal space to study in

You considered the obvious practical questions about setting up a study space when you read Chapter 1 of *The Good Study Guide* (pp. 11–12), but now you have a lot more to think about. How important is it to be able to study in a 'personal' space, where you can think your own thoughts? Apart from gaining new knowledge, studying a course like K100 is always a process of personal development. Months of reading, thinking and reflecting on your experiences produce changes to your outlook on life. But that process can be very frustrating if you are surrounded by the bustle of your daily life, constantly tugging you back into familiar ways of thinking and reconfirming you in long established roles. Sometimes you need 'personal space', to think things out for yourself – particularly in the run up to an essay. Will you need to go to a library to find it, or can you arrange a place in your home?

Section 2
Attachment to place

In Unit 1 we considered some of the issues around attachment to people and in particular the influence of Bowlby's research on mother and child relationships. Here we are going to consider the way in which people identify and become attached to places, buildings, objects, and how this attachment can contribute to personal well-being or how we feel about ourselves (Low and Altman, 1992). Looking at why places become important provides a basis for asking questions about what happens when people have to move, a common occurrence for people in need of care services.

At the beginning of Unit 6 we listed a number of ways we can think about our environment. These were physical, social and psychological. You might want to look back at how these were defined. We have spent some time looking at the first two, now we focus on the psychological environment, how experiences of places support self-identity, contributing to well-being. Given that the domestic home is a central place for most people it is not surprising that much research has looked at the meaning of home and its importance across the life course, especially during periods of home making and home maintaining which can have different effects for men and women (Arias, 1993; Sixsmith and Sixsmith, 1990; Rubinstein and Parmelee, 1992). I will start this section by considering the meaning of home.

2.1 The meaning of home

In Unit 6 you looked at some aspects of the home, how it is seen to embody the family, the association of women's lives with home and domesticity, and the way housing has been designed. Here the focus is on meaning. Many people spend a lot of time at home, they invest part of themselves within it, both materially and emotionally. So what does it mean?

Activity 10

Allow a few minutes for each section of this activity

What does home mean?

(a) The good news
Read through these comments and write down at least two important meanings of home which you feel emerge.

- 'It's family, it's where we live.'
- 'It's somewhere I feel safe, I'm always glad to come home.'
- 'It's somewhere to shut out the rest of the world.'
- 'I can be myself at home, I feel really settled.'
- 'It's comfortable, I've got this place just how I want it.'
- 'A place where all my things are around me.'
- 'It's familiar, I know where everything is.'
- 'It's financial security really, it's a place that we own.'

Comment   How did you get on? I thought there were a number of important meanings emerging from these comments. For example home is seen as:

- a place where the family live
- a secure place
- a private place
- a familiar or known place
- a place for possessions.

These themes tell us something about attachment to place and how the home can engender feelings of belonging, security, safety and permanence – all feelings which can enhance self-esteem.

But is this always the case? Do you recall occasions when you have not liked your home? Have you ever heard people say bad things about their home? Not all experiences of home are positive.

Allow a few minutes   **(b)   The bad news**

Once again, read through these comments and note down two important meanings which you feel emerge here.

- 'I can't get upstairs anymore and the roof leaks.'
- 'I never really settled here, it always felt temporary – my home was where I used to live.'
- 'You couldn't call this home, you can't swing a cat in here it's so small and there's no room to put any of your things.'
- 'I don't want to go home, I'm scared.'
- 'I've experienced homelessness in the past, so a dream house to me is four walls and a roof over my head. At present I'm stuck in bed-sit land. I've lived in one after another for a number of years. It can be really depressing.'
- 'I haven't been out for weeks, just looking at these four walls, it may be home but it feels like a prison.'

Comment   In these comments you can see a range of negative views which contrast with the positive feelings about home expressed above.

You might have thought about the following:

- that the physical environment can affect just how you make yourself at home
- that the permanence of the situation affects how settled you may feel
- that a poor environment can be depressing
- that being alone and not being able to get out can lead to feelings of isolation
- that who you live with, and your relationship with them, can make the home a fearful place and make you feel insecure.

So while most people tend to express positive views about their home, the experience of home can be both positive and negative and you will probably have noticed that some of these positives and negatives are opposites. For instance:

- security versus insecurity
- rich environment versus poor environment

- permanence versus impermanence
- safety versus fear
- belonging versus rootlessness
- somewhere that enhances self-esteem versus somewhere that demoralises.

But this does not mean that everything is always this clear cut – people can experience positive and negative feelings at the same time. For example a place may be important psychologically because it has connections with the past but it may offer a poor physical environment which no longer meets a person's physical needs. This can be a common experience for some older people.

Key points

- Attachment to home and place is one of the ways people preserve self-identity.
- Some service users have to move away from a place to which they are attached in order to receive care.
- Home can mean different things to different people.
- People can experience positive and negative feelings about their home at the same time.

These themes all tell us something about how people become attached to particular places. The following sections look at three aspects of attachment in more detail. First, how places become personalised. Second, the way attachment to place may relate to group identity as well as personal identity. Third, how the immediate home and its surroundings can become an important practical, social and psychological resource.

2.2 A place for possessions

Home decorating!

One of the ways homes come to reflect something of the individual is through the things within them. Again the nature of this *personalisation of space*, as it is called, can be socially and culturally specific but it is a common experience. Yet many people living in care settings do not have the opportunity to make the environment their own, and moving between places can mean that possessions can get lost on the way. We will come back to this issue of loss later on in the unit. First, let's think a bit more about how our attachment to place is reflected in the possessions which surround us.

Activity 11   **'Which eight things would you take with you'**

Allow about 5 minutes   The radio programme 'Desert Island Discs' asks people to choose which eight records they would take with them to a desert island. I don't want you to think about a desert island, but if you were to move to a place where you could only take a few possessions to make it your own, what would they be, and why? You don't have to come up with eight things but make a note of some items.

Comment   One of our course testers thought of these things:

- pictures of the family to remind me of people
- a personal stereo and tapes
- a clock that belonged to my grandfather
- as many books as I could manage
- a collection of little china houses that I've built up over the years – just because they remind me of places
- a quilt which I'm still making.

The things on your list probably say something about the people in your life, your interests, places you have been and would like to remember – all things which say something about you and who you are. You'll remember that some of the young people we heard from in Activity 2 talked about being able to decorate their rooms and having posters of Madonna and Michael Jackson. The importance of making a statement about who you are continues throughout life and occurs in the workplace as well as the home.

2.3 Place and identity

The last two activities show that the meaning of home and how people relate to it is complex. The circumstances of individuals and families can vary enormously and individual identity can be influenced by different levels of association with home, country, nation – a group identity. Too little is known about how ethnic diversity affects the experience and perception of home as opposed to where people see their homeland.

Sommerville, in a study of African-Caribbean British people living in Manchester, has begun to clarify these issues. Through a number of interviews he found that home was seen as very much the place where the family lived and the home area was defined in relation to a network of family and friends. Having relatives who lived in the family's country of origin was mainly responsible for preserving the sense of home as elsewhere.

He shows that with regard to attachment to home, how a person sees their ethnic identity may be more important than their stage in the life cycle – so, for example, there will be a difference between someone who sees themselves as Black English, permanently settled and integrated within British culture, who has a stronger sense of attachment than someone who sees their black identity in a wider international context – even though both might be parents of young children and of a similar age.

This is a quote from one of the people he interviewed:

> Mr E felt strongly that he had no sense of a permanent home:
>
> '... because of my particular personal situation where, being black and being British, in British society, you never truly feel at home. But by the same token if I was to go back to where my parents are from I wouldn't feel truly at home there either. So you get into the situation where home to you doesn't really have the permanence of going to your place of origin because my place of origin is a foreign country. Someone who was born in Australia [for example] but happened to be living in England would say 'I want to go home', and home to them is where they were born and raised. Where I was born and raised I don't necessarily feel at home because I'm an immigrant's son, so to speak, the son of an immigrant, so home for that reason doesn't have the sense of permanence. I can't feel at home in Jamaica because I haven't spent any length of time there, I don't know the place. By the same token I can't feel at home here because I'm not truly British, as it were. So home doesn't really mean anything permanent, I'm afraid.'
>
> (Sommerville, 1994)

The diversity in perceived ethnic identity also affected how respondents felt about their neighbourhood or the area they lived in, whether or not they felt personally secure within black or mixed neighbourhoods or a part of a particular geographic area.

To conclude then, Sommerville argues that 'the experience and perception of home cannot be understood in isolation from the issue of group identity'. His respondents talked about home in a number of different ways and he relates these to particular group identities. For example, current dwelling was associated with the immediate household group, and area of residence with the wider group of family and friends, while home expressed as country of origin meant links to a particular shared ancestral group.

Some of the different meanings of home expressed in Activity 10 may also relate to different types of group identities – being a teenager, being homeless, being a prisoner, being housebound, being part of a family with small children. It also tells us that some of the meanings which may be felt to be important for one group may not hold good for another.

2.4 Places and spaces as resources

Another factor that affects attachment to place is *time* and people involved in caring relationships, whether living together or apart, sometimes have a shared history of places. This may be true of an older couple who have shared the ups and downs of moving between places for much of their lives or a daughter caring for her mother in the home where she was born and brought up. A shared understanding of the immediate environment of the home and the support which may be available locally can prove invaluable in developing care relationships. Such knowledge becomes a resource for care. Talking to people about their experiences is one way of seeing how housing and care needs often come together.

Mr and Mrs Bright at home

Activity 12   Housing histories

Allow about 10 minutes

Pauline Bright lives with her husband, Alan, in a semi-detached house on a large estate in Bletchley. They are both in their 70s. In 1994 Mr Bright began to develop a dementing illness and Mrs Bright has been the principal carer, although she now shares the care with a number of different formal carers. In Activity 9 you heard from June Blakeway, Mr Bright's home carer. Here Mrs Bright is talking about the place and the house they live in.

Read through the extract below. Think about the different ways Mr and Mrs Bright are attached to the place and the house they live in and note down at least two important factors.

We came here in 1956, that's 40 years ago. We were living in a flat in London, in somebody's house, and it was quite comfortable, but it was going to be demolished — you know as part of London being sorted out after the war. Also we had two small children and we were going to have a third, so that was one of the reasons why we needed a bit more room. And also the house was going with the job, my husband is an engineer, and there was a lot of small engineering firms opening up here and there was one particularly good one. All the people in this road were employed in engineering, so we were very much all of a muchness. They said that in this particular road that these 12 houses were reserved for people with breathing problems because it was supposed to be healthy. They came and vetted us first and I had a history of breathing problems. I've always felt very healthy here.

The schools were new, so that's why we knew it so well because we all took our children to school. We were all very much into each other's families although we weren't all the sort of neighbours that pop in and out but we knew each others failures and successes, particularly the children. It's a good place. It's certainly turned up trumps now because of all our problems. They're all grandparents now and we've seen them come and be carted away in a hearse, you know, and all the grandchildren coming is a wonderful feeling.

I was a secretary before I married and then I was 17 years at home with the children, and then all of a sudden they wanted teachers in the 50s and 60s. There was a teachers' training college here and they were asking for people who were interested, so off I went to college, which was absolutely superb. My husband was – I asked him first – he was keen and supportive and so, after two years in college, I taught up here for 17 years. Seventeen seems to be in my mind rather a lot, doesn't it.

[Later] When we could buy houses we went around looking for what we could afford and we always came back to this one. It's east and west facing so you get the sun and also the south sun as it comes around. If you can imagine it, it's sunny all the time, all the time. It's convenient, as you can see the furniture hasn't changed much, it's lovely, it's good, everybody loves their home here. They've all left home but they all come back and squash into it somehow and the garden's just about the right size, and it's been good on and off, a few horrible things happening to everybody.

Comment

For Mrs Bright there is a long association with place and a strong sense of *attachment* to and familiarity with this particular neighbourhood. As a *place* they originally came because of employment but they have been a part of the development of a neighbourhood which seems to go beyond just place to engender a sense of belonging and community spirit. It is a place of *people*, of families where the children all went to school together, and where people continue to offer each other support. Part of this familiarity is born of the length of *time* they and many of their neighbours have lived in one place. They have also been of similar ages and part of similar households and this has meant that they have shared common activities. So they have developed *social relationships*.

Their house itself is also a place to which they are attached. It is talked about with affection – it's lovely, it's good. It has also been a healthy environment. Mrs Bright says 'everybody loves their home here. They've all left home but they all come back and squash into it somehow'. So the home also means people as well as the physical environment.

As we saw in Unit 6 where people live and who people live with are dependent on a myriad of factors. These factors combine personal characteristics and circumstances with the opportunities and choices offered in any locality which themselves will be influenced by national, social and economic policies. There will always be a wider political environment to add to the immediate environment of the individual and their family. Mrs Bright's account is a good example of how the physical, social and psychological environment are all intertwined.

To summarise then, attachment to place is a concept that brings a number of factors together and may involve:

- attachments to buildings, spaces, objects
- places that vary in scale, specificity and tangibility
- people (individuals, groups, and cultures)
- social relationships
- time.

(Adapted from Low and Altman, 1992, p. 8)

Key points

- Personalising space is a way of saying something about self-identity.
- Different understandings of group identity can affect the way people think about home and home area.
- Understanding more about the shared histories of places and spaces may be important in understanding the resources which are available to any caring relationship.
- The environment can become a resource for caring.

Study skills: Managing time

Are you finding time to fit every bit of K100 in? If not, you will not be alone. Part-time students usually have too many other commitments to be sure of completing everything. In the end, you can only learn as much this year as you have time and energy for – and if you skimp on some bits of the course, and even miss others, that doesn't mean you will fail to develop the main ideas. Like many other important things in life (such as bringing up children) learning is not an exact science. People beat their own paths to understanding. We have tried to set out a structured sequence of study activities to lead you towards certain concepts and information, but your mind will trace its own course of development through the various elements of K100. So don't feel defeated if you're not finding your way into every corner of the course. All you can do is try your best to set aside some chunks of 'quality time' (as they say) for studying each week. Keep reflecting back on what have been your best study sessions. What seem to be your best times of day or times of the week? How can you protect them? And how can you avoid frittering the time away when you have it? So long as you keep finding something approaching the recommended 12 hours a week, you will learn a great deal from K100.

Section 3
Changing places

Thinking about attachment to places leads us to think about just the opposite: how do people feel when they have to change places and move from one situation to another? Some people are always on the move while others seem to stay put for long periods of their lives. For children and adults receiving care services moving between places may be a common occurrence.

These moves may be:

- *daily*, part of a shared pattern of care where a person lives at home but attends a day centre or day hospital
- *intermittent*, such as respite care which may happen for a week or a fortnight every four months
- for a *limited period* of life, such as a young person's move from a children's home to a foster family
- *permanent*, such as moving from home into a residential home or nursing home in later life, or moving out of a long-stay hospital into alternative accommodation.

This final section of Unit 7 will consider changes in place, looking at some of the issues of space, access and attachment already discussed in the unit. This type of change will also be set alongside other changes in life and those factors which can make change a positive or negative experience will be considered. First, we look at short-term changes of place.

3.1 Change on a daily basis

Activity 13   **Caring for children**

Allow about 5 minutes

> *We leave our flat at about 8.15 am and go to nursery where Sabrina (who is four) stays for the mornings. I then take Tristan (who is nine) to school and then go on to work. Maureen, who's a registered childminder, fetches Sabrina from nursery after lunch and they go to Maureen's house. Around 3.25 pm Maureen and Sabrina go up to school and, depending what day it is, they fetch Tristan and some other children. Some days Tristan goes home with his friends as they are have a swimming lesson or football club. Either I, or Michael, fetch the children home from Maureen's or elsewhere, any time between 5.30 or 6.30 pm depending who's doing what and who's back first.*

This was written by one of the mothers whose children go to Maureen's, the childminder you met earlier. In this scenario the children spend different parts of their day in different places, so their *care is shared*.

(a)   Make a list of the various places in which the children in this scenario are cared for and how these change with time.

(b)   Think about these places and make a note of how they might be different from each other in terms of the spaces they occupy.

Comment (a) The children spend different times of the day in different places, so there are changes in both *time* and *space*. For Sabrina this includes her own home (a flat), nursery, her childminder's house, and then back to her own home. Her brother, Tristan, goes from home to school and then to Maureen's or someone else's house before coming back home.

(b) Both nursery and school will differ from a domestic home because they are group settings and include a number of children and adult workers occupying the same space. They will have been designed or adapted for the purpose. As we have already noted, Maureen lets the children in her care have access to much of the space in her house. The environment is domestic with a few modifications for purposes of safety and to enable the children to have a play space.

A baby arriving at a childminders

This activity introduces the idea of changes in time and place. The care provided by the childminder is a substitute for parental care given while the parents are working. In the case of Mr Bright care is shared between his wife and formal carers and changes in the place of care are primarily to give Mrs Bright a break.

Activity 14 **Shared care**

Allow about 30 minutes Central to this activity are Mr and Mrs Bright. You have just read some of Mrs Bright's feelings about coming to live in Bletchley 40 years ago and living in her community. Mr Bright, a former engineer, has Alzheimer's disease (see the box on page 88 for further information) and lives at home with his wife. His illness has affected his short-term memory and as a result he repeats things. Whilst he is quite physically fit and active, he has also lost control over some of his former personal skills such as washing and going to the toilet. Further background details are given in the Media Notes and you might like to read these now.

Listen now to the next part of section 2, still on side 1 of Audio Cassette 2. This part of the tape has been arranged to give you a sense of how Mr Bright is cared for during the day. It begins and ends with Mrs Bright. You should listen to the whole sequence and stop the tape after Mrs Bright has told us that Mr Bright is 'glad to go' to bed. Begin by just listening to this sequence which will take about eight minutes. Then rewind the tape to the beginning of this sequence and listen to it again. This time try to answer the following questions:

(a)   How is Mr Bright's care shared and why?

(b)   What does this mean for Mr Bright? Does he have any control over the situation? How does he react to changes in time and place?

(c)   What does this mean for Mrs Bright – how does she react?

Comment   (a)   Mr Bright's illness places great demands on his wife but they are determined that he should stay at home and so his care is shared between their home and a day unit. Mrs Bright rises early and is in constant attendance on her husband. I don't know about you but I felt quite tired listening to her speak. I could almost hear the relief in her voice when she said 'By 8 o'clock I know June's going to come'. In this case, even though Mr Bright is seen as the client who June comes to 'wash and dress', it is also Mrs Bright's needs that are being met. June is one of three home carers who assist Mr Bright with getting up and going to bed. June says that she 'doesn't do anything for Mrs Bright' – well not in the official sense of the word. But listen to Mrs Bright say 'It's such a relief. It's lovely to have all this going on in the house'. Here care is shared, June knows that her work only makes a 'temporary difference' ... 'you can't make a permanent difference but you improve things for a while'.

Mr Bright also attends a special day unit for older people with dementia. But it seems again that Mrs Bright's needs are central to the provision of this service. Brenda Masters says 'Alan's been coming here since January. He started off coming here three days a week which very quickly went to five days, the need is very great there for Pauline, his wife, to have some time to herself really, she was getting very tired, very stressed'.

Chatting in one of the day rooms

(b)   For Mr Bright the consequence of this shared care is that other people attend to him in his own home and he also leaves it for part of the day. His condition has meant that he has had little control over the situation. Care has been provided to support Mrs Bright in her caring. However, this has also meant that Mr Bright has lost some of his personal privacy. He is now assisted in a number of intimate tasks by a formal carer who has access to his own personal space. You will remember how June coped with this invasion of privacy as a care worker.

A bus comes to take Mr Bright to the day unit, so at this point he becomes someone else's responsibility. How does this change of place affect him? Well it's difficult to tell but listening to Brenda Masters at the day unit we do get a sense that he feels disoriented and dislocated. She says that he needs a lot of reassurance. We noted earlier in the unit that many people feel disoriented and anxious in unfamiliar settings; however because of his short-term memory loss, the day unit may seem unfamiliar to Mr Bright *every* day. Every day he may have to negotiate both people, place and spaces as if for the first time. Brenda says:

We welcome Alan as he arrives off the bus. He needs guiding into the unit, he's quite disorientated and he may go off down the drive. We encourage him to sit down and have a cup of tea and calm him down because he's quite anxious, we'll sit with him and try to do something on a one-to-one basis. He does enjoy talking but finds focusing on any sort of topic for a length of time quite trying. He gets lost and confused and his mind blocks. He likes to get up and walk around – he's quite an active person, he has a lot of energy. During the course of the day he requires a lot of reassurance and orientation.

(c)   For Mrs Bright, Mr Bright's absence means a breathing space. It gives her some privacy. She attends to herself – moving the main meal of the day to lunch time so that she can cook and eat properly; going out (on this day to the Carers Support Group) and spending time on her hobby, playing the piano.

Mr Bright has to face change on a daily basis, moving between individual and group care. While we do not hear about it here, he also goes for the occasional week's respite care in a nearby residential care home (see the Media Notes). At the time of the interview Mrs Bright told me that a recent experience of respite care had not gone so well: Alan had been to another home which was unfamiliar and this had unsettled him. Familiarity of place and being able to orient yourself is all part of feeling in control over your everyday life. For Mr Bright, whose illness creates further disorientation, familiarity of place and routine are even more important.

The Brights' routine now includes shared caring to meet some of their different needs. Yet at the heart of their situation is a determination that Mr Bright should remain living as much as possible in his own home maintaining some continuity in his life and familiar surroundings.

Dementia and Alzheimer's disease

Dementia is a condition characterised by a progressive loss of mental abilities accompanied by changes in behaviour and a gradual decline in the skills needed to carry out ordinary daily activities. The likelihood of developing dementia increases as people get older. It affects less than one person in a thousand of those below the age of 65 and between four and five in a hundred of those over 65. In the over-65 age group there is a strong increase in the rate with age: about 2 per cent of those aged 65–75 suffer from dementia, rising to over 20 per cent of those over 80. It is estimated that there are 650,000 people with dementia in the UK.

There are a number of different types of dementia. Alzheimer's disease is the most common type accounting for 50–60 per cent. The disease was first described by Alois Alzheimer, a German neurologist, in 1907. Symptoms vary from individual to individual. In the early stages the person may be more forgetful of recent events, more likely to repeat themselves in conversation, less concerned with activities or other people, less able to grasp new ideas or adapt to change, more anxious about having to make decisions, or more irritable or upset if they cannot manage a task. As the disease progresses, loss of short-term memory is likely to become more obvious and people often become confused about time and place. In later stages they may no longer be able to recognise those who are close to them and become increasingly dependent on others for care.

(Adapted from Alzheimer's Disease Society, 1997)

At this point it is worth noting the similarities and differences which exist between the pattern of Mr and Mrs Bright's lives and Sabrina and Tristan, the children who spend parts of their day at the childminder's house. While their needs are very different, both the children and Mr Bright have to make transitions between different people and places. The importance of maintaining continuity of people and places is important in both cases. Many people attend day care services and find that the change is a stimulating experience, widening their daily contacts and allowing them to become part of another group. The issues of continuity of experience raised here will be familiar to day care workers.

Activity 15   **The Redwood Day Unit**

Allow about 20 minutes

Now go on and listen to the rest of side 1 of Audio Cassette 2. In the remaining part of the tape you will hear Brenda Masters and Ceinwen Conroy talking about the Redwood Day Unit. As you listen, think about how the environment of the unit and the way the staff work help to minimise the dislocation someone like Mr Bright might feel.

Make some notes about (a) the ways of working discussed here and (b) the environment.

Comment (a) **Ways of working**. The whole ethos of the Redwood Unit is one of maintaining a calm environment where people can be themselves. Pressure is not put upon people to take part in activities. There is even something rather calming about the way Brenda and Ceinwen speak. Brenda says 'activities are spontaneous here' and that 'levels of ability vary from day to day'. The key to working here is flexibility. Enhancing ability rather than focusing on disability is important, and part of this comes from getting to know people and their past lives. This also involves those at the day unit in reaching out into the community and not seeing themselves as a separate service.

Ceinwen and Mr Bright sharing memories

(b) **The environment**. There are a number of things which are raised about the environment, especially orientation, use of space and safety. The unit was set up partly because another day centre used by older people was felt to be too big for people with dementia. Some settings can produce disorientation or make a condition even worse. Did you notice how Brenda says that there are two lounges and these are used by different groups of people – those who 'can tolerate small groups' and those who 'need more space'?

The open plan nature of part of the unit allows some people to wander in safety. You will have also heard Ceinwen talk about the secure nature of the unit and the way in which they manage wandering. A tension exists here between the needs of people to wander – even to get back home – the needs of carers for respite and the needs of staff to be able to manage how they work in the unit with the resources they have available. How these various interests are balanced becomes crucial in many care settings.

The design of units for people with dementia has become a particular area of interest in recent years as designers and architects have been concerned to create environments which help people to maintain the abilities that they have, for example colour coding of floors or walls to assist orientation, and to help manage certain kinds of behaviour, for example a wanderer's garden or route layout (Marshall, 1993; Dunlop, 1994).

In this case we have been able to look at how shared care has implications in terms of time, space and place for all the people involved. Mr Bright's illness has led to decisions being made about the place of care. The aim is to enable him to retain his home base and this means supporting Mrs Bright by giving her some respite from caring. This has meant that Mr Bright has less control over where he spends part of his time and he has to adapt to relocation in time and space and to changes from individual to group settings.

Having home care has also meant allowing other people to have access to their home. For Mrs Bright this level of access has been accepted as it means that Mr Bright can continue to live at home. In this case the change of place has been daily and always involves a return to home, but for other people receiving care the change may be more long term and of greater permanency.

> **Key points**
>
> - Receiving care can involve changes of place for different periods of time from daily changes to long-term changes.
> - Sharing care between informal and formal carers can mean that those on the receiving end of care have to accept changes in time, space and place. This can be disorienting for some people and stimulating for others.

3.2 Relocation

We have seen that attachment to place can be important in terms of developing and maintaining feelings of security and a sense of self-identity. However, care for some people involves relocation.

Changes of place often involve people in coping with other types of change such as:

- changes of role (for example from being a homeowner to being a resident of a home; or from being a hospital resident to being a resident in the community)
- changes of status (for example, from being a child to adult, from being unemployed to being employed).

While the focus here is on place, the importance of these others changes needs to be taken into account. They are often interlinked. So for example a change in place may give rise to a change in role.

All change demands some personal or psychological adjustment, although some situations will be experienced as more stressful than others. If you look back to Section 2.4 of Unit 6, you will see that the people facing a move in the research by Hudson *et al.* saw 'fears of (and subsequent adjustment to) a major change of environment and living circumstances' as a major obstacle to moving (1996). How people cope with adjustment is at the heart of change. In terms of changing places this can often relate to their attachment to where they have come from and to the impact which moving may have on their self-identity which we talked about earlier in relation to issues of belonging, permanence and security.

Activity 16   Losing your home

Allow about 20 minutes

Read Chapter 9 in the Reader. Here the author talks about what she sees as the devastating effects that moving can have on an older person. As you read the extract try to answer the following questions:

(a) How does the author Peter Marris, who is quoted in the article, describe the experience of losing your home?

(b) What may help people cope with a change in place?

(c) What may be the negative effects for older people of moving into an institutional setting?

(d) How might moving from one care setting to another increase the likelihood that older people may be less in control of the situation?

Comment (a) Marris equates losing your home with bereavement or losing a close relative. He comments on the anger, grief and pain experienced by people who have lost their homes through urban renewal schemes, and it is suggested that older people may experience similar feelings when moving into sheltered housing or residential care through losing their home, their neighbourhood and their possessions.

(b) It is suggested that if people can recreate their social status and way of life within a new place then they will work through their loss.

(c) However, older people may find it more difficult to 'make a positive effort to identify with their new life' and this is seen as one of the reasons for the high death rate among some older people during the first year after 'relocation'. It is often those in poor health who do not survive the move.

(d) For some older people moving from hospital back to their own home may be more difficult due to what Norman calls a closing up of their 'social space'. In other words, the support which they had before going into hospital may break down and this may lead the person to have far less choice over where they are discharged to, often having to move to either a residential care home or a nursing home.

For some older people entering residential or nursing home care means a devaluation of their past lives and a loss of self. In this case relocation may involve enormous loss, especially if the move has been relatively unplanned and from hospital without the opportunity to say goodbye to your home.

The research discussed in Chapter 9 of the Reader suggests that the degree of control which the individual exerts over the moving process is crucial to how they adapt to such change.

Activity 17

Allow about 5 minutes

Read through the case study of Mr and Mrs Smith who moved first to a residential home and then later became separated. What are the main differences between the initial move made by the Smiths and the later moves? What factors have affected how they have coped with these changes?

The Smiths

Mr and Mrs Smith were a couple in their 80s who had decided to move into residential care because of the increasing frailty of Mr Smith and the stresses this placed on his wife. They chose the home partly because they already knew people there, and they appeared to settle in well. In the first interview after their move, Mrs Smith expressed relief at having more support and the reassurance of readily available help, and the couple spent some evenings visiting or being visited by other residents. Although Mr Smith complained of having 'too much leisure', they both felt that the purpose of their move had been achieved – the stress of caring for Mr Smith had been taken over by the staff.

Two months after their move, Mr Smith had a stroke, and was admitted to the local hospital. From there he was discharged to a nursing home nearby as the residential home did not have the staffing mix appropriate to his nursing needs. This left the couple in two different establishments. Mrs Smith could not follow her husband to the nursing home because the higher cost prohibited this and they were financing their care themselves. If the cost had been affordable, however, there were other objections – the Smiths did not know anyone at the nursing home and the move would mean leaving friends. When visited by the researcher at this time, Mrs Smith recounted the story, sometimes breaking into tears when she thought of her husband, but interspersed her story with rationalisations and justifications which seemed to be partly derived from the discussions she had had with the staff in the home and her family. She showed no anger about the decisions which had been made about her husband's care and her response seemed to be to accept the situation as one over which she had no control: 'Well you have to go where is suitable, haven't you'.

(Reed and Roskell Payton, 1995)

Comment   The main point to strike me about this case is the level of control the Smiths were able to exert over their first move and the subsequent loss of control. Their first move appears to have been a conscious decision on their part. They moved into a setting where they had friends and were able to adapt to their new circumstances. It has been Mr Smith's subsequent ill-health which has led to their separation. This vulnerability has meant that he needs more nursing care and has had to be accommodated in a nursing home. They have also lost financial control over the situation. It is interesting that one of the reasons Mrs Smith did not want to move to the nursing home was because she would lose contact with her friends. So the Smiths demonstrate some attachment to the first residential home which they would lose if they both moved. By staying, Mrs Smith maintains these contacts.

Of equal importance in terms of adjustment is an acceptance of the new situation and identification with the new life (Lieberman and Tobin, 1983). Reed and Roskell Payton (1995) have shown how 'adjusting to life in a care home is a complex process, requiring a range of social skills'. They have observed a range of strategies from those people who '"push" themselves on strangers' to those who 'construct familiarity' using what little they know about people and places to find common bonds and therefore permit conversation. They also show how within our present system of long-term care for older people, changes in a person's physical or mental health may lead to further transitions: the most common is from a residential care home to a nursing home. Such additional moves may further unsettle a fragile equilibrium as this case showed.

In many ways this experience is paralleled by others receiving care. In Unit 6 we saw that far more young people in care live with foster families than in children's homes. The transitions from children's home to foster care, between foster families, and to independent living involve not only changes of place but enormous changes in status and role from child to adult. Research has shown that many young people in need of care have experienced multiple moves and that the support offered before, during and after leaving care may be far from adequate (Marsh, 1997). In Unit 9 we shall be exploring some of the issues which help or hinder such changes for young people and the skills needed to support those moving between care settings.

3.3 Models of adjustment

Here we have talked about changes of place as having a particular impact on an individual's sense of well-being or self-esteem. Relocation and separation from familiar places just like separation from loved ones can be experienced as a form of loss which can have devastating effects for some people. Some authors have seen changes in self-esteem as the key to understanding how people cope with change. For example, Hopson and Adams (1976) suggest that any transition, whatever triggers it, sets off a cycle of changes in self-esteem. They provide a model which suggests that individuals may experience similar patterns of feelings and emotions within the process of adjustment.

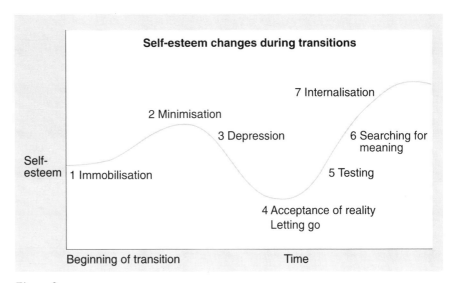

Figure 2
A model of changes in self-esteem during transitions (Hopson and Adams, 1975, p. 13)

Here the key to successful adjustment to change is to work through this cycle of reactions. But not everyone will experience all these stages and some people may become stuck along the way, for example experiencing on-going depression. Here are some of the key features of each stage.

Immobilisation. You get a sense of being overwhelmed, unable to act. Unfamiliar transitions, and those of which we have negative expectations, tend to intensify this stage.

Minimisation. As a way of coping with the change it is common to deny that it is happening. This is a frequent reaction to a crisis which is too difficult to face.

Depression. People often get depressed when they face up to the implications of change.

Accepting reality. At this point the person begins to let go of their old state of being, accepting the reality of what is happening to them.

Testing. Having begun to accept the situation, then it becomes possible to test out new behaviours to cope with the new situation.

Seeking meanings. This is a reflective stage where people try to work out how and why things are different.

Internalisation. Finally, understandings of the situation and new meanings become internalised and accepted. They then become part of the person's behaviour.

(Adapted from Hopson and Adams, 1975, pp. 9–12)

You can see that some aspects of this model have already been touched upon in Alison Norman's article and the discussion of Mr and Mrs Smith. For older people 'accepting the reality' of residential living and constructing a new sense of self late in life is particularly important but there are obvious parallels for people of all ages who face major life transitions. We will be looking in more detail at identity in Unit 14.

There are other models of coping and adjustment which are based on stages. Some consider how people work through losses in their lives, perhaps one of the most well-known being the stages model of grief developed by Parkes (1986) in his work on bereavement. Such models are useful in allowing recognition of the process of adjustment although not everyone conforms rigidly to set patterns (Sidell, 1993).

Key points

- Changes of place can involve people in coping with changes in role and status.

- All change demands some personal or psychological adjustment. Coping with changes of place can relate to attachment and losing your home can be equated with bereavement.

- Personal control over changes of place is important in relation to how people cope and adjust.

- Models have been developed to help us to understand the process of change and the effects on self-esteem. However, models can seem prescriptive.

Conclusion

In this unit we have explored further the relationship between people and places as part of the care relationship. We have looked first at how public and private space is defined and the importance of this distinction in terms of the activities and roles of those involved in care. Access to space is seen to be crucial in defining space both in the home and in care settings. In particular we have looked at how access to and control of space can place limitations on people's lives.

An important aspect of private space is the way it can reinforce the ability to find privacy. Maintaining privacy has become a key issue within residential care settings and we have seen that privacy is a complex topic which can be dependent not only on place but also on interactions between people which are influenced by issues of age, gender, class, culture and social roles.

In the second and third sections of this unit the focus has been on attachment to places and the relationship between place and identity. The domestic home is seen as a place where people can maintain some control over their lives and yet many people receiving care services have to leave their homes or move between places. How people cope with such change is an important issue in care work and we have considered some aspects of the process of adjustment. The theme of working with people in changing circumstances is picked up again in Unit 9. In Unit 8, we move on to consider the lives of people who live in care, but before you leave this unit, take a few minutes to reflect on the core questions posed at the outset.

Study skills: Keeping your spirits up

When you are studying independently it is very important to keep up your morale. As a part-time student it is very easy to 'drop out' in a bad week. You don't have to leave university and go home. You simply stop studying and get on with all the other things in your life. So it is essential that you keep your sights on what you are hoping to get out of studying the course and don't let temporary set-backs put you off. For example, if you get stuck and can't seem to understand the point, give yourself a break, or move on to something else. Or, if you have made contact with some other K100 students, perhaps you might phone one of them and get a new angle on things. (There is information on forming telephone networks and self-help groups in the K100 Introduction and Study Guide.) Another time you might want to make contact with a fellow student is when you get an assignment back from your tutor. We can all feel very sensitive about what people say about our writing and talking to someone can help to put things into perspective. For some students, attending tutorials is a very important way of keeping up morale. Hearing other people talking about their experiences makes you realise that it's not just you who runs into difficulties. Sometimes it is helpful to talk to people close to you, even though they are not studying the course, just to get things straightened out in your own mind. You might also phone your tutor, though you should check whether some times are unsuitable. You will have to work out your own support systems. The main point is to recognise that studying is an intense and absorbing activity which brings lows as well as highs.

To keep you moving on through *The Good Study Guide* we have quite a short recommended reading at the end of this unit – but a thought-provoking one.

Study skills: Learning from reading and listening

Most of the vast multitude of things you have learnt in your life you have picked up in direct communication with other people rather than by formal reading. What is the relationship between learning by listening and learning by reading? Can one help the other? You can read about this in *The Good Study Guide,* Chapter 3, Section 1.

Your study diary

Finally, how is your study diary going? Are you finding time to get a few thoughts down? If so, are you finding it interesting? And does it help you to reflect and to plan? Have you worked out a set of headings to suit you? If you need to remind yourself, we suggested some headings in the conclusion to Unit 2, but these may not be the best ones for you. You are half way through Block 2 now – mid way between TMA 01 and TMA 02. Perhaps this is a good point at which to review progress and think ahead.

References

Alzheimer's Disease Society (1996) Information Sheet 1, Alzheimer's Disease Society, 10 Greencoat Place, London SW1P 1PH.

Arias, E.G. (ed.) (1993) *The Meaning and Use of Housing*, Avebury, Aldershot.

Buckeldee, J. (1996) personal communication.

Dunlop, A. (1994) *Hard Architecture and Human Scale. Designing for Disorientation: A Literature Review on Designing Environments for People with Dementia*, Dementia Services Development Centre, University of Stirling.

Gubrium, J.F. (1975) *Living and Dying in Murray Manor*, St. Martin's, New York.

Hall, E.T. (1966) *The Hidden Dimension*, Doubleday, Garden City, New York.

Hopson, B. and Adams, J. (1976) 'Towards an understanding of transition: defining some boundaries of transition dynamics', in Adams, J., Hayes, H. and Hopson, B. (eds) *Transition: Understanding and Managing Personal Change*, Martin Robertson, London.

Hudson, J., Watson, L. and Allan, G. (1996) *Moving Obstacles: Housing Choices and Community Care*, The Policy Press, Bristol.

Ittelson, W.H., Proshansky, H.M., Rivlin, L.G. and Winkel, G.H. (1974) *An Introduction to Environmental Psychology*, Holt, Rinehart and Winston, Inc., New York.

Leiberman, M.A. and Tobin, S.S. (1983) *The Experience of Old Age: Stress, Coping and Survival*, Basic Books, New York.

Low, S.M. and Altman, I. (1992) 'Place attachment: a conceptual inquiry', in Altman, I. and Low, S.M. (eds) *Place Attachment*, Plenum Press, New York.

Marsh, P. (1997) 'Child care', *Research Matters*, Community Care, Oct. 1996 – April 1997, pp. 60–62.

Marshall, M. (1993) *Small Scale, Domestic Style, Longstay Accommodation for People with Dementia*, Dementia Services Development Centre, University of Stirling.

National Federation of Housing Associations (1993) *Accommodating Diversity: The Design of Housing for Minority Ethnic, Religious and Cultural Groups*. National Federation of Housing Associations and the North Housing Trust, Newcastle upon Tyne.

Parkes, C.M. (1986) *Bereavement: Studies of Grief in Adult Life* (2nd edn), Tavistock, London.

Patients' Association (1996) 'What should be done about mixed wards? "Close them all by 30th October 1998", says PA', *Patients' Voices*, Issue No. 1, Autumn 1996.

Reed, J. and Roskell Payton, V. (1995) *Settling In and Moving On: The Transition to Care Home*, paper given at the Annual Conference of the British Society of Gerontology, University of Keele. Amended version of paper to be published in the journal *Social Policy and Administration* in 1998.

Residential Forum (1996) *Creating a Home from Home: A Guide to Standards*, National Institute for Social Work, London.

Rooney, R., Lewis, B. and Schüle, R. (eds) (1989) *Home is Where the Heart Is: Voices from Calderdale*, Yorkshire Art Circus in association with Continuum.

Rubinstein, R. and Parmelee, P. (1992) 'Attachment to place and the representation of the life course by the elderly', in Altman, I. and Low, S.M. (eds) *Place Attachment*, Plenum Press, New York.

Sidell, M. (1993) 'Death, dying and bereavement', in Bond, J., Coleman, P. and Peace, S. (eds) *Ageing in Society*, Sage Publications, London.

Sixsmith, J. and Sixsmith, S. (1990) 'Places in transition: the impact of life events on the experience of home', in Putnam, T. and Newton, C. (eds) *Household Choice*, Futura, London.

Sommer, R. (1969) *Personal Space: The Behavioural Basis of Design*, Prentice-Hall, Inc., Englewood Cliffs, New Jersey.

Sommerville, P. (1994) *The Meaning of Home for African-Caribbean-British People*, paper presented at the conference Ideal Homes? Towards a Sociology of Domestic Architecture and Interior Design, University of Teeside, September 6–8th, 1994.

Twigg, J. (1997) 'Deconstructing the "social bath": help with bathing at home for older and disabled people', *Journal of Social Policy*, Vol. 26, Pt. 2, pp. 211–32.

Westin, A.F. (1967) *Privacy and Freedom*, Atheneum, New York.

Acknowledgements

Grateful acknowledgement is made to the following sources for permission to reproduce material in this unit:

Text

p. 72: Auden W. H. 'Some thirty inches from my nose', The Estate of W. H. Auden, 1995, in Mendelson E. (ed) *As I Walked Out One Evening*, 1995, Faber & Faber Ltd; *p. 88*: Extracted from *Alzheimer's Disease Society Information Sheet 1*, May 1996, Alzheimer's Disease Society.

Figures

Figure 2: Hopson B. and Adams J. 'Towards an understanding of transition defining some boundaries of transition dynamics', in Adams J., Hayes H. and Hopson B. (1976) *Transition: Understanding and Managing Personal Change*, Martin Robertson.

Illustrations

Pp. 58, 61, 72, 78, 85: Sally and Richard Greenhill

Unit 8
Living in Care

Prepared for the course team by Sheila Peace

While you are working on Unit 8, you will need:
- Course Reader
- Offprints Book
- *The Good Study Guide*
- Audio Cassette 2, side 2
- Media Notes
- Care in the UK
- Wallchart

Contents

Introduction

While only a small percentage of the total population lives in communal settings, the chances of 'living in care' vary with age and type of dependency. The data in Unit 6 showed that a quarter of people over the age of 85 years live in residential homes, nursing homes or hospitals. Because this type of care has become such a common experience for people in very old age, this unit begins by looking at this life and the way residential living can be based on an approach to care which focuses on individual needs. These issues are explored through hearing about the lives of older people at Liberty of Earley House, a residential care home in Earley, just outside Reading, Berkshire. Liberty of Earley House provides a baseline from which we can ask questions about care settings in general – what works, what does not work and why?

The phrase 'living in care' is often thought of in a negative way. It often conjures up large institutions – the workhouse, the long-stay hospital and the ways people can become institutionalised. Here we consider institutionalisation and debates around both policy and practice with regard to residential settings. As we saw in Unit 3, the move away from institutional living to care in the community has been one of the dominant themes of social policy in the post-war period for all groups offered care by the state. Yet dilemmas still exist around residential care and its role in the future. Some of the issues discussed in this unit will be picked up again in Unit 16 which considers the closure of a long-stay hospital for people with learning difficulties. The historical development of institutions is also discussed in Unit 16 and you will probably want to reflect upon the experiences discussed here at that point.

While the *experience* of residential living has changed for some people, the *ownership* of residential settings has changed for many. The growth of the independent sector throughout the 1980s and into the 1990s brought with it a growing concern for the regulation of care settings. If the public sector was not to provide these services then they would have to regulate them. The unit ends by looking at regulation, an issue which is taken up again in Blocks 5 and 6.

Core questions

- What are the key features of a person-centred approach to care in residential settings?
- What do we mean by institutionalisation and in what ways is it experienced?
- Why do residential homes differ with some being described as more institutionalised than others?
- Is there such a thing as 'good residential care'?
- What alternatives to institutional living have been proposed?
- Should care settings be regulated?

Section 1
Residential living – a person-centred approach

1.1   Liberty of Earley House

Liberty of Earley House describes itself as a housing plus care scheme for older people and is registered with the local authority as a residential care home. It was opened in 1992 and has 26 self-contained one-bedroom flats and four studio apartments (bed-sitting rooms). In 1994 it won the 'new build' category of the Care Homes Design Awards for high standards in design and management. In this respect it is not typical of many of today's residential or nursing homes which are commonly housed either in large converted domestic houses (often with modern extensions) or in purpose-built buildings ranging in age over 50 years or more. Indeed, some pre-war and nineteenth century buildings are still used in this way.

The internal courtyard at Liberty of Earley House

I have deliberately chosen to focus on a relatively new scheme because it allows me to look at the relationship between the physical, social and organisational environments in a situation where great attention has been paid to design. Liberty of Earley House is something of a hybrid: it is a scheme which has tried to disentangle accommodation and care. All too often these two important elements become entwined – so instead of care being delivered where people wish to be, people have to move to the care. Choice over environment then becomes one of 'what is available' and 'at what cost'. At Liberty of Earley House people have been attracted to the accommodation as well as to the care offered. The importance of making a distinction between accommodation and care needs was central to arguments put forward in the independent review of residential care carried out in the mid-1980s and chaired by Lady Gillian Wagner.

> **The Independent Review of Residential Care**
>
> The Independent Review of Residential Care was commissioned in December 1985 by the Secretary of State for Health and Social Services to 'review the role of residential care and the range of services given in statutory, voluntary and private residential establishments within the personal social services in England and Wales'. Two reports were published from the review – Part I: *Residential Care: A Positive Choice* (often known as the Wagner Report) and Part II: *Residential Care: The Research Reviewed* (National Institute for Social Work, 1988 a and b). Following the work of the committee, the Wagner Development Group was set up to ensure that the recommendations made were taken forwards through setting priorities and developing programmes. The final report of this group *Residential Care: Positive Answers* (National Institute for Social Work, 1993) covers this development work and includes a review of the Caring in Homes Initiative, a programme of work in residential care funded by the Department of Health in 1989 (Youll and McCourt-Perring, 1993).

In this section you are going to hear a great deal about Liberty of Earley House – from the architect who designed the building, residents who live there and staff who work there. To begin I will consider the physical environment and the ideas which lay behind the development of this scheme.

The physical environment

Activity 1 **Designing Liberty of Earley House**

Allow about 20 minutes

Side 2 of Audio Cassette 2 (30 mins) is devoted to living and working in Liberty of Earley House and in the Media Notes you will find some background information to the scheme which you should read before listening to the tape. You may find with all the activities relating to Liberty of Earley House that you want to listen to each section of the tape more than once – so it may be a good idea if you have a counter on your cassette recorder to note down where each section ends so that you can find it easily.

The first speaker on side 2 of Audio Cassette 2 is Maurice Heather, an architect with the practice Phippen, Randell and Parkes who was responsible for the design of the house. He is part of a group of architects within the practice who have designed a number of what they call 'special needs' buildings. First of all listen to Maurice talking about Liberty of Earley House and stop the tape when he finishes speaking.

Here I want you to think about some of the features of the physical environment – such as access, privacy and environmental control – that we saw as important to the experience of giving and receiving care in Units 6 and 7 and how an architect tries to incorporate some of these features into a design for a care setting. As you listen to Maurice make a note of:

(a) those things which architects have to take into account when they are designing a building

(b)   those aspects of the physical environment which they feel enable older residents to maintain control over their daily lives

(c)   issues raised about this setting as a work environment for the staff and one which has to meet certain regulations

(d)   how it might be different from other long-term care settings you might know.

You may not have heard an architect talking about the way he or she works before. Maurice uses some technical terms such as 'single banked corridors' which means having apartments only on one side of a corridor. You came across some of these terms and ideas in the Offprints article 9 by the Matrix group refered to in Unit 6.

Comment   (a) and (b)   As an architect, Maurice is very concerned with the site, location and aspect of the building. He wants to create spaces in which people can move about easily, interact with others or withdraw into. Protecting privacy has been a key concern and the flats provide very distinct personal territory. He has been concerned that the building should be light and accessible, that the public spaces offer stimulation, and that certain requirements for safety and security are met. He is particularly conscious of providing details such as the windows by the front doors which offer a view through to the courtyard or the 'milk bottle' recesses which might add a touch of domesticity. On the other hand he is aware of the institutional nature of some communal facilities such as the assisted bathrooms.

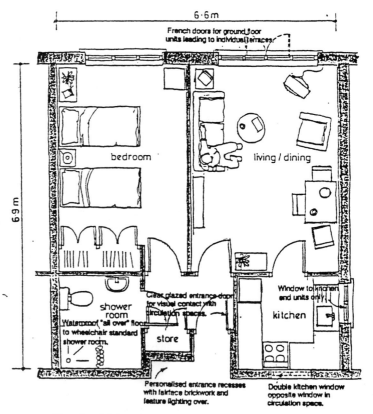

Typical Flat Plan   **45 sq m**

(c)   The needs of the residents have dominated his thinking about this building, and it is interesting to note that work had to be done at a later stage to improve facilities for the staff by converting one of the large stores into a second office. Also, did you notice how issues around fire safety prevented the architect from opening up the lounge area and giving the residents greater space for leisure activities? This is an example of how the way communal buildings are regulated may impinge upon the lives of individuals. As we noted in Unit 7 with regard to Maureen's house, registered care environments need to meet fire, health and safety regulations and we come back to this issue at the end of the unit.

(d)   Liberty of Earley House is certainly very different from many of the old people's homes I have been into and I think I would be happy to live in one of these flats. The project was privately funded so the amount of money available for development was probably more generous than in some other schemes. The amount of space provided for each individual is greater than in most care settings (45 square metres for the one-bedded self-contained flats and 27 square metres for the studio apartments). The balance of public and private space within the setting is very definitely weighted in favour of private space, and use of technology and modern appliances would appear to support personal control. It is better resourced than many residential homes for older people although single rooms and *en suite* bathrooms are more common in the mid-1990s than they were in the mid-1980s.

Architects' drawing of Liberty of Earley House

You will have noticed from Maurice's comments that while he had lots of his own ideas for the building, he was also given a brief by those representing Help the Aged and the Liberty of Earley Trust. He didn't talk to potential residents of the scheme, but he was advised by people with a lot of experience in developing housing for older people. His brief was to combine a sheltered housing environment with the communal features of a residential care home. These ideas are in line with findings from the research by Willcocks *et al.*, which you read in Unit 7, where older people living in residential care were asked about the environments they wished to live in. It was not surprising that people wanted what the researchers called 'unexceptional, normal, non-institutional' private space, control over everyday aspects of their lives like the temperature in their rooms, and a sense of safety – features which were incorporated at that time into a model for a residential flatlet (Willcocks *et al.*, 1987).

It is worth remembering at this point that a majority of older people living in residential care are women and that some of the issues raised in Unit 6 about the design of the home and women's roles take on a new meaning here (Women's Design Service, 1991). As you also saw in that unit, directly involving service users in consultation processes over the design or adaptation of buildings is still far from common, as Maurice Heather's colleague Mike Tuck commented about the some of the briefs they receive:

> We don't know to what extent they are management led or occupant led. Whether there's a balance there ... it's sometimes difficult to understand that.

Most residential schemes for older people designed by Phippen, Randall and Parkes are likely to be commissioned by a housing association with housing corporation funding. Given that these schemes will be less generously funded than Liberty of Earley House there is usually less space for the residents – commonly 25 square metres for a bedsitting room.

Ways of living

But how much does the physical environment matter? At Liberty of Earley House the generous allocation of private space says something about the way each occupant is valued as an individual. But the quality of the physical environment may just be a bonus. Of greater importance may be the social environment – the people and how they interact. Before you hear from the staff about their ways of working listen to some of the residents talking about their lives in the house. What do these views tell you about their quality of life?

Activity 2   **Ways of living**

Allow about 20 minutes

Carry on listening to the tape. You are going to hear four residents in the scheme talking about their lives – Freda Cooper, Roddy and Jenny Matheson, and Joan Price. Switch the tape off after Joan has spoken. As you listen to each of these residents make a note of:

(a)   the ways these residents cope with the various activities of daily living

(b)   how they are supported by the staff and the physical environment.

Do you feel that these older people are able to maintain their own identities and ways of living within this communal setting?

Comment   **Freda**

Freda moved to the house from another residential home because of increasingly poor health. She is very definite in her views about not wanting to go and live with her daughter and son-in-law, a common view among many older people. However, life at the house was not like her own home. About the move she says 'At first, I not exactly resented it, but I thought it's not like my house, I didn't do this, I didn't do that, but I've got nowhere else to go'. Thinking back to Unit 7 and the ideas about relocation, one senses that Freda has made an adjustment, she talks with acceptance rather than resentment. She has made a choice even though it was her health which precipitated the move.

She talks about the importance of the physical environment given her poor sight and her arthritis. She values aspects of the environment such as the space which she has deliberately left uncluttered. However, she has also had to lose possessions of value to her such as her rug, and she still has problems with those high cupboards and that shower. She manages her breakfast and having a wash which, although it may sound an ordeal to you or me, she speaks about with great determination.

The shared care which she achieves with the staff is reflected in the way she says 'we cope between us' and she acknowledges that she is part of a group when she talks about her twice weekly baths – 'they'd do it more but of course there's too many of us to fit in' . Although it is obvious that she needs the assistance of staff such as the cleaner – that 'splendid little girl' – there is also the sense that they don't do things the way you might want – 'they don't move a great deal'. But you can also sense from these comments that she has control over the situation, and her comments over the cleaner display the power of class differences. Life has become full of compromises in some respects but there isn't a sense of staff taking over her life. She is managing to do what she can herself and her own assessment of the home presents a positive picture.

Roddy and Jenny

Roddy surrounded by his books

Roddy and Jenny moved to the house from sheltered housing. Jenny has particular problems with mobility and Roddy had been doing most of the caring. He was finding it hard going. At Liberty of Earley House he is relieved of some of those aspects of physical care – cooking, cleaning, washing. It is Jenny who experiences more intimate personal care. You will have noted what she says about the lift which 'they [the care staff] say is a great help to them'. She does not say what *she* feels about the lift; rather there is acceptance that this will be a 'help for nurses' backs'. She has had to make a compromise to enable people to help her.

When it comes to washing herself she 'rings for a certain person' and once again she is determined to take over as soon as she can. She also says that 'someone is supposed to come and push me down to lunch' so there is a sense here that sometimes this does not happen, and frustration is reflected in the comments about wanting to get out into the garden. These are things which Roddy used to help her with which she now has to rely on others for, and in this case the others are busy – 'they're always pressed for time, there are a lot of people with different needs'. Again here is the recognition of living within a group where staff time is finite.

Joan

Joan is a new resident at Liberty of Earley House. As you heard the whole process of moving into the house was quite hurried and Joan had to make some quick decisions. In particular she had to adjust to living in a small flat having moved from a bungalow.

You will have heard Joan talk about Tracey as her keyworker. We will be looking at these ideas in a moment. Tracey has obviously enabled Joan to go and do her own shopping. Joan's concerns about her diet have also been accommodated and she feels she can move freely in and out of the house. She does not sound resentful about the fact that she has to 'put my name down on a board so that they know where I am in case of fire'. This is an example of the way individuals need to be accounted for when living in group settings, something which we would not necessarily think about in the course of our daily lives.

In each of these interviews with residents we can see how they are able to protect their own identities by the way care is negotiated. It is obvious that their routines have to some extent become adjusted to those of the home but there is flexibility here. The physical environment offers a degree of both autonomy and support but it will never compensate for the human needs of these residents. Freda, Roddy, Jenny and Joan have all had to make compromises but there is a strong sense that they remain in control of their lives. How is this achieved?

Joan in her flat. Remaining in touch with other people is important

Ways of working

If residents appear to be finding residential living a positive experience, then alongside their own resources and the physical environment we need to consider the home as an organisation and the care provided. From what the residents say, the staff have developed ways of working that allow residents to be themselves, or at least to make decisions about as many aspects of their lives as possible. Listen to what some of the staff have to say about their work.

Activity 3   **Ways of working**

Allow about 15 minutes

This part of the tape includes contributions from Ann Hamilton, care manager, Mary Bennett, deputy, and Marion Whitehead, senior care assistant. As you listen write down the key words which staff use to describe their ways of working.

Switch the tape off after Marion comments about the involvement of families in the house.

Comment   The words which I thought summed up their approach to care work were: enabling, negotiating care, keyworking, shared care, providing continuity.

Let's look at some of these words and how they are used in more detail.

Enabling

Ann put the aims of the house in this way:

> *We try to provide a spectrum of care dependent on the needs of the individual, and we encourage people to be as independent as they can within the home. We try to act as **enablers**, so that when somebody moves in here it's still their home, we only give input as necessary, but they've got the security of knowing that there is always somebody there.*

Their approach is one which lets the resident take the lead over what they can or cannot do for themselves and to try and offer care 'as necessary'. They also recognise that people have diverse needs and so they offer a 'spectrum of care'. Finally, Ann acknowledges that what they offer older people is the security of knowing someone is there. These ideas are reinforced by Marion's comments that 'it doesn't matter how long a task takes, it's just so important that they do things for themselves as much as they can'. This is very different from taking over all the tasks and decisions that people have to make in their lives. It is an approach which allows people to retain their own identity. They are 'people first' and the fact that they may have a range of physical and mental health problems is not allowed to override this fact. These views are very similar to those expressed by Esther Hurdle when she spoke about her first experience of home carers in Unit 7.

Negotiated care planning

In standing back the staff need to know how and when to intervene. To do this means really getting to know people and, as we heard, in Liberty of Earley House this is done informally through everyday conversation and more formally through developing *joint care plans* and *negotiating changes* through *assessing risks*. This means discussing with people what they can and want to do for themselves, and the risks involved for them as individuals and as a part of a group. The word *negotiate* is therefore key here. This approach raises the rights of residents to take decisions and the risks and responsibilities that this entails.

Compromise

The staff, by taking on the role of enablers, help people to carry on taking control of their lives. Liberty of Earley House is a very open institution, open to people's ideas and needs. At the same time residents did say that there are occasions when staff are too busy to meet all their needs but on the whole this is accepted as a part of living in a group. Residents therefore appear to recognise compromises and are prepared to make them. Perhaps making compromises may be easier from a position where you still retain some control.

Keyworking

Care planning is carried out by keyworkers allocated to each person. While staff rotas mean that keyworkers are not always available, at Liberty of Earley House flexible work patterns for staff allow them to undertake a wide variety of activities with residents. This includes just having a chat which has been shown time and time again in research to be one of the things older residents value from staff (Peace *et al.*, 1997).

The staff here are committed to their work and they themselves are well supported. Team working and training are seen as important and we shall be looking more closely at some of the skills involved in care planning in Unit 9.

Shared care and continuity

Finally you will have heard Marion talking about involving family members in care where the resident wishes this to happen. This openness to sharing care also places value on *continuity* in people's lives and is one which is supported by groups like the Relatives' Association which stresses that family members may often feel they have no role to play when a close relative moves into a care setting (White, 1994).

Liberty of Earley House can be seen as a good example of residential care which supports the lives of individuals who live as a group.

Key points

- The design of the house has given residents sufficient private space and facilities to undertake self-care, maintain territorial control and protect their privacy.
- Residents are people whose past lives contribute to their present circumstances. Attempts are made to maintain continuity with family and friends.
- Staff acknowledge resident control over private space.
- Staff approach care through negotiations with residents over personal responsibilities and risk-taking which can be renegotiated as care needs change.
- Staff are valued as a group and supported in their work.

Study skills: Learning from audio cassettes

The audio cassettes are where you are put directly in touch with the real world of care provision. Did you feel that listening to the architects, the staff and the residents of Liberty of Earley House gave you a well filled-out mental picture of how this type of accommodation works? At the end of Unit 7 you read about the connection between reading and listening. Did the cassette give you better insight into the concerns the designers and operators of Liberty of Earley House are trying to address than you would have picked up just by reading? Did it help you to get into the 'language' of planning and organising residential care and accommodation? Were the words in the text easier to read because of what you'd heard? It's worth reflecting on these things because the more you understand your own learning processes the more sensibly you can make decisions about what time to give to what activities – and the better you can judge when to keep going with what you are doing and when to give up and start something different.

1.2 Underlying principles

We are now going to look in more detail at some of the underlying principles of practice in residential care demonstrated here. What do you think should be the basis of good residential care practice?

Below are summaries of good and bad points about residential care made by residents, relatives, friends and visitors who gave personal evidence to the Independent Review of Residential Care (NISW, 1988). This evidence erred on the side of the positive. However, the following reservations were mentioned:

> *The majority of correspondents have been motivated to write by enthusiasm for good residential homes or indignation at bad. It may be expected that the number who have 'mixed' opinions are greater than their representation in this sample suggests, since those with less extreme experiences will have had less incentive to write.*

> *(1988, p. 159)*

The Wagner Report

The Wagner Report said that correspondents appear to be unhappy in homes where:

- cruelty, ill treatment or neglect are overlooked by those in charge

- admission has not resulted from a resident's own considered decision

- regimes are designed for the convenience of an inadequate staff rather than to maintain the choice and comfort of residents

- activities and outings are few or non-existent

- visitors are not made welcome

- food, furnishings and facilities are poor

- there is no respect for residents' dignity, individual personality or ability
- conversation, shared enjoyment and affection are not valued or encouraged.

Correspondents appear to be happy in situations where:

- admission has been the resident's own choice
- there is good food, warmth, physical and medical care, and provision for disability
- furnishings and facilities are satisfactory in both public and private areas
- services such as chiropody and hairdressing are available
- visitors are always welcome and there are facilities for entertainment
- there is provision for a variety of activities and outings
- birthdays and special occasions are celebrated
- the resident is free to come and go or choose what to do at any time
- relationships are such as to allow the use of Christian [sic] names and reassuring physical contact
- conversation and companionship are encouraged both between residents and between residents and staff.

(NISW, 1988, pp. 138 and 146)

Underlying these statements are some basic values of human life. You looked at the way values underpin this course in the Introduction and Study Guide and at the end of this section you may wish to look back and compare that discussion with these statements concerning residential care.

Activity 4   Underlying values

Allow about 5 minutes   Look at these statements and make another list, this time of the values which you feel are expressed here. For example you might think that the fact that the resident is free to come and go or choose what to do at any time is saying something about *autonomy*.

Comment   I thought these statements said something about the following values:

- privacy
- autonomy
- choice
- dignity
- self-determination
- integration, with the wider community.

Some of the literature on practice in residential care

These values or similar lists are commonly quoted in the literature on practice in residential care. For example you will find discussions of all of these in documents like *Home Life: A Code of Practice for Residential Care Homes* (Centre for Policy on Ageing, 1984), and the recent revision *A Better Home Life* (Centre for Policy on Ageing, 1996) as well as the Residential Forum document *Creating a Home from Home* (1996).

In the Wagner Report five interrelated principles were outlined, which taken together were felt to form the basis of good practice in residential care:

Caring	This should be personal, and residents should feel valued, safe and secure.
Choice	Each resident's right to exercise choice over their daily life should be respected.
Continuity	This includes both consistency of care from staff, and the maintenance of links with a resident's previous life.
Change	For residents, the opportunity for continued development; for staff, a commitment to respond to changing needs.
Common values	Ensuring that practice is based on a shared philosophy and values.

(Adapted from NISW, 1988a, p. 60)

Codes of practice with underlying principles such as those set out here are now becoming commonplace and many settings will have their own written philosophy of care and charter of rights for residents. But what becomes more difficult than identifying principles is putting the principles into practice. Again the Wagner Report stated: 'It is true that what we have to say has been said many times before; the question remains, why has it not been consistently translated into practice?' (p. 61). This is really the key question about residential living and leads us to ask:

> *Why do residential homes differ with some being described as more institutionalised than others?*

Before trying to answer this question we are going to consider what is meant by institutionalisation and the way it has come to dominate thinking about residential care.

Key point

- There are some basic principles for residential living which are underpinned by core values including privacy, autonomy, choice, dignity, self-determination and integration.

Section 2
Institutionalisation

Institutions have a dark and controversial history. For example, the workhouse in the nineteenth century developed in relation to the Poor Law to accommodate people who were destitute and either too old, too young or too frail to find work. The Board of Poor Law Commissioners applied the 'principle of lesser eligibility' so that people who received relief should not be able to experience conditions of life as good as, or better than, those experienced by the 'independent labourer of the lowest class' (see Townsend, 1962). It created the categories of deserving and undeserving poor – ideas that still have resonance today.

One of the prime functions of this system was to act as a deterrent to the so-called work-shy. Consequently the physical and social environment was harsh as these comments testify:

> *Middle-class visitors entering a workhouse for the first time could be deeply shaken by the harsh indignity of the prison-like routine, the grotesque, despairing and toothless faces, 'the forlorn half-dazed aspect of these battered human hulks who were once young'. There was no need to write up the words 'abandon hope all ye who enter here'. George Lansbury [1928, p. 135-6] wrote of the Poplar workhouse, 'The place was clean: brass knobs and floors were polished, but of goodwill, kindliness there was none'.*
> *(Thompson et al., 1990, p. 37)*

The Victorian legacy of the work ethic and the workhouse has been influential in moulding attitudes towards institutions today. Quotes such as these conjure up pictures of groups of people crowded together and subjected to harsh regimes with very little opportunity to be treated as individuals. As you will see in Unit 16, changes in the provision of institutional care for children and adults have occurred throughout the twentieth century as the move towards community care has gained momentum. Yet a growing number of very old people come to live in group settings at the end of their lives. Workhouse buildings still

Mid-morning in one institution, from Townsend's The Last Refuge, *1962*

survive as care environments, whilst others have been replaced by modern alternatives, and although current views on care practice condemn the ways of the workhouse, aspects of institutional life remain. In this section we focus on the characteristics of institutional life and what is meant by institutionalisation.

2.1 Characteristics of institutional life

So what were, and are, they like, these institutions which have stayed with us throughout the twentieth century?

Activity 5   Characteristics of institutional life

Allow about 20 minutes

Turn now to Chapter 1 in the Reader. Read through at least two of the pieces in this section. Then read them again, this time making a list of any aspects of the lives portrayed here which these accounts have in common.

Comment   While I can't tell which pieces you read, there are a number of things which these accounts have in common. I thought the following stood out:

- a feeling of hopelessness and despair
- the lack of privacy
- the lack of personal choice
- the lack of personal dignity
- the lack of control over everyday living
- the lack of stimulation
- the rigid nature of routines
- the way people are depersonalised and treated as a homogeneous group with no past and no future
- the strict discipline and the way staff seem to need to be in control
- the pressure staff are under and the sense that there are not enough of them.

A homogeneous group is one where everyone is the same.

You may feel that these descriptions of institutional life are very different from residential settings today. They may seem too harsh or too negative. But perhaps some of these features sounded familiar: even if you have never been in such a setting you may have read about situations which had some of these features.

If you look back you will see that some of these points are similar to the views expressed by those with unhappy experiences who wrote to the Wagner Committee in the 1980s. What you have begun to do here is identify some of the features of institutionalisation which researchers have observed and recorded over a long period of time.

2.2 The process of institutionalisation

In 1959, a British consultant psychiatrist called Russell Barton wrote a monograph called 'Institutional Neurosis' in which he proposed that 'patients came into mental hospitals with one form of illness, and hospital itself could give them another' (Jones and Fowles, 1984, p. 71). While his work centred on mental hospitals he was making the general point that the institutional environment itself can have negative effects on people. He described the symptoms of this 'disease', as he saw it, as 'apathy, lack of initiative, loss of interest in the outside world, submissiveness and resignation' – a kind of learnt helplessness. He also pointed to 'clusters of factors' which he claimed were the cause and which could be tackled.

- Loss of contact with the outside world.

- Enforced idleness, e.g. due to ward routines.

- Bossiness of medical staff and nursing staff.

- Loss of personal friends, personal possessions and personal events.

- Drugs, e.g. use of sedatives to produce apathy and make patients manageable.

- Ward atmosphere, e.g. poor furniture, dirt, smell.

- Loss of prospects, e.g. losing touch with family, unemployment.

This list connects with some of the areas identified in Activity 5.

Barton's concern to define the 'symptoms' of institutionalisation bears some similarity to the research into institutions carried out by the American sociologist Goffman whom we met in Unit 4. In his book *Asylums* (1961), Goffman presents a number of arguments about institutional life which have influenced the way many people view institutions. His study of life in a large mental hospital enabled him to consider the similarities and differences between a range of institutions. He was also one of the first people to consider institutional life from the perspective of service users or inmates, as he called them, rather than that of the senior staff or members of the management.

Asylums is made up of four papers, the first of which, 'On the characteristics of total institutions', presents a model which identifies four main characteristics that distinguish 'total institutions'. He is not suggesting that these characteristics always occur but that they can occur and are related to each other.

Activity 6   **Goffman's total institutions**

Allow about 30 minutes

In Chapter 8 in the Reader you will find a summary account of Goffman's work on total institutions given by Jones and Fowles from their book *Ideas on Institutions*. You will probably need to read this piece twice. On the second reading make notes about:

(a)   what Goffman meant by a total institution

(b)   the four main characteristics of total institutions.

Comment   (a)   The concept of total institutions can be visualised in terms of a continuum from open to closed institutions. Towards the closed end of the line we find institutions which can be described as 'total' – 'a place of residence and work where a large number of like-situated individuals, cut off from the wider society for an appreciable period of time, together lead an enclosed, formally administered round of life.' Examples of total institutions are said to include homes for the aged, mental hospitals, prisons, boarding schools, monasteries.

(b)   Goffman's four characteristics are:

Batch living, where people are treated as a homogeneous group without the opportunity for personal choice. Activity is undertaken en mass. Rules and regulations dominate and residents are watched over by staff.

Binary management, where there are two worlds of residents and staff which are seen to be totally separate, with staff wielding power over residents through maintaining distance between them.

The inmate role, where people who come to live in institutions are stripped of their former roles, made to break with the past, lose their personal identity and become an inmate.

The institutional perspective – over time the inmate may come to accept the loss of self and the power of the institution.

Goffman cautions that not all these features apply to all total institutions. However, they provide a very useful check-list for examining what a particular institution is like and many researchers have used these concepts. For example, in 1968 King *et al.* developed the Resident Management Practices Scale for use in children's homes (King *et al.*, 1971). This measurement instrument distinguished four dimensions of institutional life which varied between settings:

* the rigidity of routine

* the block treatment of residents

* the depersonalisation of residents

* the social distance between staff and residents.

Others have focused on how the two worlds of the residents' living environment and the staff's work environment co-exist. The power or strength of the institution as an organisation can mean that everyday life may become more organisation-centred than user-centred (Peace *et al.*, 1982; Willcocks *et al.*, 1987).

Understanding the characteristics of institutions through writers such as Goffman helps to explain the process of institutionalisation. Researchers have argued that it is through the experience of rigid routines, block treatment and depersonalisation that residents begin to exhibit the signs of apathy, dependency and loss of autonomy which Barton saw as a 'disease' and which can be called institutionalisation. To become institutionalised is to be so used to living in an institution that living independently seems impossible.

Goffman's work has been influential in terms of both research and practice within residential settings. However, some would argue that the model has been taken too much at face value with little understanding of the complexity of the arguments. One group of experts in the field of residential care recently had this to say about the influence of Goffman in relation to care for older people:

> *For some older people there is still the lingering fear of the workhouse and its stigma, while for many social workers, the only standard text on care in a Home that they will have been recommended will have been Goffman's 'Asylums', a useful but dated and one-sided view of large old institutions. This thinking has been translated into a view that the needs of the organisation may take precedence over the needs of the individual and that all care in a Home is damaging. The consequence is an emphasis upon care for people in their own homes, diversion from care in Homes and the creation of alternatives, such as staffed sheltered accommodation and supported group homes. The result has been a welcome variety of provision with the potential to offer people real choice. However, the negative images of care in Homes lingers on.*

> *(Residential Forum, 1996, p. 12)*

These ideas have had a powerful influence on the study of care settings but is this analysis dated or can all care settings result in levels of institutionalisation? The Wagner Report posed the question 'why do the underlying principles for residential care often seem difficult to translate into practice?'.

The fundamental questions we must ask are:

- Is it the nature of institutional living or living *en masse* that creates institutionalisation?

or

- Is it the dependent status of those groups of people who find themselves in institutions which prevents them from living 'ordinary' lives? (see Baldwin *et al.*, 1993).

To try to answer these questions we are going to look at a variety of settings and some aspects of institutional care.

Key points

- A number of writers have been influential in trying to assist our understanding of institutions and institutional life. This is particularly true of Goffman's work on total institutions.

- Total Institutions may be characterised by a number of features including lack of privacy, choice and personal control, rigid routine, block treatment and segregation.

- Institutionalisation is said to develop as a consequence of institutional life, but the dependent status of the people receiving care may also be a factor.

Study skills: How many notes should you take?

In Block 1 we discussed several times how to mark texts and take notes as you study. You also read Chapter 2 of *The Good Study Guide*, where different kinds of notes were demonstrated (p. 48) and a range of benefits of note taking were discussed. So have you settled down to a text marking and note taking routine? Or are you wondering whether it's worth the time and effort? Could you be using the time better on other things? Perhaps you are taking too many notes – will you have a use for them, given that you have the printed texts to go back to? These are important questions, because you need to use your time and energy effectively. We gave a strong emphasis to note taking in the early units because we wanted to establish the idea that you cannot learn much by passively scanning the words of the texts – you need to engage with the ideas behind the words and make them your own. But you have to experiment and reflect, and work out for yourself what patterns of reading and note taking achieve this for you. In the end you want a range of styles and a flexible approach so that you can adapt to different kinds of study tasks. Don't slavishly take lots of notes out of a sense of duty. Do what works.

Section 3
Institutional care, residential living

In this section we are going to look at a number of care settings for different groups of adults and children and relate them to Goffman's model of total institutions. Can a distinction be made between institutional care and forms of residential living which people find a positive experience?

3.1 Variations in care

Activity 7   **Cedar Court: an institution?**

Allow about 15 minutes   Turn to Chapter 25 in the Reader. This is the chapter about Cedar Court you looked at first in Unit 4. Read the chapter again up to the section headed 'Punishment'. Think about Goffman's work and his four aspects of total institutions and make a note of any of these features which occur in Cedar Court.

Comment   When I looked back at Goffman's four features of total institutions I felt that Cedar Court could be regarded as offering institutionalised care. There are many aspects of 'batch living' described here; people are treated as a homogeneous group, with little choice or personal privacy. The idea of 'binary management' also seems strong with interactions between staff and residents being very well defined. While we do not hear directly from the residents in this piece, the way staff speak of residents reveals a loss of individuality. They have become people to be talked over and talked about, who have little privacy and little dignity. Issues around abuse in communal settings are taken up in Block 6.

In contrast with Cedar Court it would be difficult to talk about Liberty of Earley House as a total institution. But why is this?

Activity 8   **Institutional care, residential living**

Allow about 15 minutes   Read Chapter 25 one more time and answer the following questions:

(a)   How does Cedar Court differ from Liberty of Early House in terms of:
- type of setting
- physical environment
- ways of working
- quality of life for residents?

(b)   How would you summarise the main differences between these settings? Are there any similarities?

Comment   (a)   **Type of setting.** Cedar Court is a nursing home, whereas Liberty of Earley House has been registered as a residential care home. This could tell us that the people living in Cedar Court may have greater mental or physical health problems and be less able to help themselves than people living at Liberty of Earley House.

The physical environment. The contrast in the physical environments of these two settings is stark. At Liberty of Earley House great attention was paid to creating an environment which was seen as housing plus care, whereas at Cedar Court the image is of a hospital-like environment which is drab and uniform, from the magnolia paint to the bedroom furniture. While some people at Cedar Court have personalised their rooms, others have little of their own, and some people still have to share space with up to four people.

Ways of working. Again the comparison could not be more different. I have already discussed the philosophy of Liberty of Earley House with its focus on enabling residents to be themselves and maintaining autonomy. At Cedar Court there seems to be a hierarchy between professional and auxiliary staff which establishes certain patterns of working. Auxiliary staff appear under-valued and unsupported. They see their work with the older residents as tasks to be done, not people to be enabled. They have objectified the residents.

Staff routines dominate at Cedar Court. There is an early morning tea round with night shift workers wishing to 'present the patients to the new shift intact, clean and quiet in their rooms for 8 am.' The morning shift then spend a lot of their time getting patients up and ready to come into public areas of the home. The observations recorded here are in direct contrast to the negotiated shared care which we heard about from residents at Liberty of Earley. There we heard Jenny, who had many problems with mobility, talking about 'taking over' her own washing. Lee-Treweek's research shows how people can be depersonalised by staff who ignore their presence, and are treated as objects and labelled. She says:

The two auxiliaries dress George with a running commentary to him about what they are doing. Once finished they lift him into his chair. They go to leave without a word to George. Lucy turns to the other worker and says loudly as they exit: Right, that's done.
(Reader, Chapter 25)

Quality of life. What would make life worth living in these two settings? At Liberty of Earley House residents are encouraged to remain in control of their own lives with staff assisting and facilitating. At Cedar Court quality of life seems bleak just with very basic needs being met – food and shelter.

(b)   Some of the main differences between the two settings include:

Cedar Court	**Liberty of Earley House**
• a lack of resources	• resources – financial, environmental, staffing
• residents' dependency in terms of their mental or physical health which makes them vulnerable to staff insensitivity and abuse; residents are not seen as whole people	• residents make a positive choice over accommodation and care; they retain control and are enabled to be themselves
• distance between staff and residents	• interdependency between staff and residents
	• high staff morale and staff support

The only similarity I thought of was that they are both fairly segregated environments. While the residents of Liberty of Earley House still go out and have contact with family there did not seem to be much interaction with the local neighbourhood.

Institutional care or residential living?

This activity has focused on some of the extremes of good and bad practice in residential and nursing home care for older people.

It can be argued that in the type of environment witnessed at Cedar Court people may become institutionalised. But to go back to the earlier questions – is the institution to blame or does this say something about the value attached to those people who come to live in care?

While we do not know how much it might cost to live in Cedar Court or the resources available to those who own or manage the home, this is a 'poor' environment in which to live or work.

The physical environment of residential and nursing homes has gradually improved and there are many examples of good care practice (Laing, 1996; Peace *et al.*, 1997), yet living somewhere like Liberty of Earley House is something few experience.

Current research shows that older people are less likely to move into a residential care or nursing home:

- if they have informal support in the community and if that support can be maintained

- if their income is sufficient to maintain or enhance that support at home and delay a move to residential care

- if their socio-economic status is higher rather than lower

- if their housing environment is conducive to coping with levels of disability

- if their lack of resources is compensated for by community services.

(Adapted from Peace et al., 1997)

They are more likely to move to a care setting if they live alone, need care services three or four times a day and have a dementing illness (Opit and Pahl, 1995). So issues of individual vulnerability and dependency coupled with financial resources may make some older people more or less prone to experiencing institutional care.

So far I have focused on residential settings for older people and aspects of institutionalisation. But how far do the ideas and the questions raised about institutional care have meaning for other people in different circumstances? Here we consider three different situations: care at home, care for children in an assessment unit and residential care developed by black groups.

3.2 Institutional care at home

Can people who receive care services at home, or in a day care setting, also feel institutionalised?

Activity 9

Allow about 5 minutes

Institutionalisation at home?

Imagine that you are a middle-aged woman living alone in your own flat. You are recovering from a stroke. Home carers come in and help you to get up, wash and dress in the morning and undress, wash and go to bed at night. You receive meals on wheels three days a week and two days you attend a day hospital where you receive some rehabilitation. You pay privately for a cleaner who comes in twice a week on Mondays and Thursdays. As you have difficulty with the stairs, a neighbour organised for your bed to be brought down into the living room. Your nephew and his wife visit about once a month as they live some 200 miles away. Given what we have learnt so far about institutionalisation, would your life feel institutionalised in any way?

Comment

I thought I might feel my life had become constrained and less flexible. I now have to fit in with the routines of all these people who are now coming in and out of my home. I would have become one of many people who has to be seen, so this might seem like batch-treatment. I may dislike the time the home carers come to help me go to bed, I may dislike the food which meals on wheels bring but I may feel I have to eat it as I would otherwise have to go without. However, being at home would give me a feeling of being in control, I would still be surrounded by my possessions, and people would know who I am and where I live. But the degree of control would very much depend on how much I could remain in charge. I might feel that I was losing some control over my home but I might be wary of complaining about the way things are done in case I lost the services.

Gavilan (1992), who has looked at the similarities between institutions and home in relation to issues of dependency and control, uses Goffman's analysis to assist her. She comments:

> Goffman notes: 'In civil society, for much of our activity, the judgement and action of authority are held off and one is on one's own. It is at our own discretion to delay eating, leave a task to join a friend, get up late etc.' He comments that it is not so in institutions where there are timetables for rising, eating, bathing etc. So it is for the house bound who have to fit in with the requirements of the organisation, which in

turn has to attend to a large number of peoples' needs. Goffman comments that 'self-autonomy is violated in so many simple things'. He notes that 'this process of social control is present and in effect in all organised society, but we forget how detailed and closely restrictive it can become in an institution'.

Home care for the frail and house bound does something very similar. It opens up the minutiae of personal life for examination and questioning by outsiders, strangers, authorities. The most simple and previously taken-for-granted actions and needs have to be made public and humbly requested ...

(Gavilan, 1992, p. 11)

In the case of people who are housebound you can see that dependency can also lead to a form of institutionalisation at home; however here the environment can support self-identity – if not total privacy or dignity. The individual can at least maintain some of their own established routines and this can give a sense of security. These ideas link to the discussion of access, privacy and relocation in Unit 7.

There are other situations where being dependent can lead people to be at the mercy of other people even for a short period of time. You will remember that in Section 4 of Unit 2 we talked about the hospital environment and commented on Lupton's review of patients' experiences where recurrent themes were helplessness and loss of control. She equated the hospital with a total institution.

Northenden Road Children and Young People's Resource Centre

3.3 Children in care

In Unit 6 the data for children living in care showed that a relatively small number lived in children's homes and more children lived with foster families. The role of children's homes has changed over time and many now offer short-term care while assessment is carried out before a child is placed with a family. Here we look at a children's home where practice is changing to reflect new ways of working with young people. How does Goffman's analysis of total institutions relate to this setting?

Activity 10

Allow about 20 minutes

Home truths

During the course of 1996, the magazine *Community Care* ran a series of articles about different children's homes to tie in with a Department of Health campaign to promote good practice in residential care for children. In the Offprints Book you will find an account of one of these – Northenden Road Children and Young People's Resource Centre – which is a short-term unit in Manchester (Offprint 11). The article also includes comments from a lay inspector who visited the centre for a day.

Read through it now and think what kind of environment it is. Does it show any aspects of institutional care? How might it be seen as home-like? It might be useful to think about some of the headings we used earlier:

(a) type of setting

(b) physical environment

(c) ways of working.

You may also find that it helps to read through the piece more than once.

Comment   (a)   This unit for eight to ten children and young people over the age of 12 years offers assessment and accommodation, and the ratio of staff to residents is high. The children and young people are described as 'troubled and troublesome' with challenging behaviour. They have all experienced family breakdown and some have had trouble at school, with the law and with how they feel about themselves. Compared to the older people we met earlier their needs may seem very different on the surface but they are all dependent on others and perhaps what they share is a need for accommodation, support, stability, security and people who will enable them to be themselves and understand themselves.

What was a children's home for 22 years has now become a 'children and young person's resource centre' and yet the residents refer to it as a 'children's home'. The expected stay is six to eight weeks but the 'reality is closer to six months'. I began to wonder about the impact of these differences on residential living – do you become attached to a place in six months? Does a 'resource centre' feel like home? But then here the aim is to move on, not to stay and so perhaps this *is* a centre of resources, and accommodation may feel secondary to issues of family relations, education or health.

(b)   The physical environment offers mixed messages. The young people interviewed by Paul Newton talked about the location and its accessibility to amenities: this was important to them – it wasn't a segregated facility. He talks about part of the actual building being 'cavernous and institutional, though efforts have been made to minimise the negative effects'. All the residents have their own room and there is discussion of the way the kitchen, the family room and the lounge have been changed to make them less institutional. However, the young people are unhappy with not being consulted over the bathrooms and how staff facilities are wallpapered while their facilities are painted. I wondered whether they were more concerned about status than with the physical environment and yet they have been involved in personalising the lounge area with a statement on which they can all connect, 'Let's kick racism out of football'.

(c)   The article talks about how staff are learning to work in new ways which means taking account of anti-discriminatory practice, enabling young people to understand their rights and finding ways to work with them in areas which test the boundaries such as over issues of restraint. Here the focus on rights is strong and is also seen in the access offered to external advice or an independent visitor.

Central issues for staff at Northenden Road are the importance of good communication, the keyworker or linkworker system and staff training and support.

At Northenden Road staff appear to have recognised how the physical environment and their ways of working can encourage institutionalisation and they have been actively trying to restore the balance between the needs of the organisation and the needs of the individual. Some of the similarities and differences between this setting and those you have looked at for older people could be summarised as follows.

Similarities: issues of dependency, need for resources, dealing with challenging behaviour, control over the environment, personal space, need for consultation, risk-taking and responsibility, concern over personal control, importance of communication, keyworkers.

Differences: short-stay versus long-stay care, emphasis on being a resource unit not a long-term home, emphasis on rights, meeting needs for education, concern for the developing adult.

3.4 Black perspectives on residential care

Home from home

Northenden Road has shown that settings for children and young people can have some different priorities from those for adults. Now we consider the experience of people from minority ethnic groups who live in care settings. Until fairly recently the social needs of children and adults from minority groups living in care have been overlooked, they have been incorporated into mainstream services, their experiences marginalised and the issue of racism ignored (NISW, 1993). The Wagner reports were criticised for failing to explore the experience of black people in care, both as residents and staff. As a result research has been undertaken to explore this perspective focusing not only on mainstream provision but also services run by the black community. How might they measure up against Goffman's analysis of institutions?

Activity 11

Allow about 30 minutes

Black perspectives in residential care

Turn to Chapter 11 in the Reader which summarises the findings of a study by the Black Perspectives group set up by the Wagner Development group. The study explored projects which were specifically set up to provide residential care for black people and this extract looks particularly at black leadership, practical care and issues for staff. Begin at Section 1 'The experience of black residential projects'.

As you read, answer the following questions.

(a) What are seen as the advantages of black-led residential care?

(b) What components of practical care contribute to a person-centred approach?

(c) What can affect the way staff work with black residents?

(d) How would you describe this provision; is it a form of institutional care?

Comment

(a) The main advantage of black-led residential care advocated here is being able to develop a clear philosophy 'which encompasses an agreement of needs based on the acknowledgement, understanding and experience of racism'. The approach is holistic – cultural identity is not just about visual expressions of culture which may occur in mainstream homes (and can serve to mask racism). The authors comment that in mainstream homes racism is often dealt with as an afterthought and staff have to be 'convinced, trained and cajoled into an understanding of racism and its effects'.

In black-led homes black children are accepted as part of the black community and the view is expressed that the care of black children should incorporate care by black adults. In black-led homes older people share common bonds and have a sense of being valued. Black projects may be smaller than mainstream care homes.

(b)   A number of areas of practical care were explored which contributed to an approach to care which respected both personal and group identity. These included:

  •   various aspects of language – not only the ability to communicate but also common understanding of the language used in organisations

  •   use of natural medicine and the value of older people's views on health matters

  •   regular meetings of residents

  •   real choice, for example over food

  •   the involvement of family where this is valued

  •   shared faith.

(c)   Staff often had little opportunity for formal training but they organised their own in-house. The keyworker and counsellor systems are used with children but not with older people. They felt this was not the only approach although importance is attached to clear care plans which 'provide opportunities for people to say what help they need and negotiate how this help is given'.

An important feature of black-led homes is the relationship between the home, its staff and the wider community. There is an interchange of people coming in and out of the home. Multidisciplinary working is encouraged, teachers and other professionals have direct involvement in the home and staff are usually a part of the local community, living nearby. In this sense the homes are integrated within their community. Where desired there is a shared approach to care with family members. There is also a recognition that issues of attachment can be local, national or international. This relates to Sommerville's research concerning group identity that we looked at in Unit 7.

(d)   The way this form of residential care is described it does not feel like institutionalised care. While all forms of residential care are institutions these projects feel open rather than closed. There is a holistic approach to care which is developed through care planning and encompasses shared care with the family. Perhaps more than any of the examples you have looked at in this unit there is a sense of integration between community and institution bonded by the shared experience of racism. This contrasts with the way mainstream homes are often viewed as segregated services within the community.

In this section we have explored some of the positive sides of residential living and some of the negative sides of institutional care. As Cedar Court indicates, examples of total institutions are still to be found. The other settings have shown not only how institutionalisation may emerge at home but also how approaches to care which acknowledge the needs of individuals and groups can overcome the power of organisational routines and practices. You have begun to explore some of the differences and similarities that exist between different settings. Issues of dependency and resources are important factors for all people who may experience some form of residential living.

In returning to the questions posed at the end of Section 2, it may be fair to conclude that the experience of institutional care relates to both (a) the dependent status of the resident, and (b) the type of physical and social environment. A difference does exist between residential living and institutional care.

Key points

- Residential living can be a positive experience. This can depend on issues of resources and the maintenance of autonomy through negotiated care planning.

- Institutional care can be a negative experience where individuality is denied through batch living.

- Aspects of institutionalisation can occur in domestic and day care settings.

- In care settings for young people issues of rights and personal development may be more prominent than in settings for older people.

- Black-led homes offer an important opportunity for the development of a holistic approach to care which incorporates the experience of racism within its basic philosophy.

Study skills: Difficult words

As you study you keep coming across new and often long words such as 'institutionalisation', scattered among other long and sometimes similar sounding words, such as 'institution' and 'normalisation'. And then you get a discussion about 'residential living' as opposed to 'institutionalisation'. What's the difference? Aren't they both to do with long-term living in shared (non-family) accommodation? How are you supposed to get to grips with this?

Do you try to guess what the two terms mean, look them up in a dictionary, or just make a little detour around them and keep ploughing on? One problem with standard dictionaries is that they don't necessarily have 'social science' words listed – or they give a definition which is the everyday meaning, not the social science one. Getting hold of a social science dictionary is one option – though the definitions given are sometimes quite complicated, and meanings may vary from one area of the subject to another, so they are not always as helpful as you'd hope. Anyway, I looked up 'institutionalisation' in the hefty two volume *Shorter Oxford Dictionary* and found it was not listed. However, at the bottom of the paragraph under 'institutional' I found 'institutionalize'. The first meaning given was 'to render institutional'. This didn't seem very helpful. But the second meaning given was 'to bring up in an institution'. This seems fairly close. But it doesn't quite fit as an alternative to 'residential living'. And the definitions given for residential were entirely unhelpful.

So dictionaries are often not the answer. In fact the clues you need are often in the unit itself if you stop to think. In this case, you need to link the term 'institutionalisation' back to Goffman's writing about total institutions. Here, institutionalisation refers to the state people are often reduced to when they live for long periods in institutions – passive, rule-following, depressed. The term stands for what we want to avoid when people have to live together. It is a negative word. Consequently, in order to be able to talk constructively about how people can be accommodated together, we need a different term. We decided that 'residential living' would be sufficiently neutral.

Section 4
Challenges to institutional care

Debate about the nature of institutions and the effects of institutional life throughout the second half of the twentieth century has led to a number of movements for change. Ideas have been developed which offer alternatives to institutional care; some challenge its very existence and others develop different models of provision. This section looks at three influential sets of ideas:

- normalisation
- home and family as models for residential living
- collective living.

4.1 Normalisation

The idea of 'normalisation' was first developed in Scandinavia in the 1960s in relation to services for people with learning difficulties. Taking into account Goffman's critique of institutions, people began to discuss how to improve the lives of service users by advocating that 'services should seek to maximise the quality of life of service users by reproducing the lifestyle experienced by non-disabled citizens' (Emerson, 1992). They tried to:

> ... model life, even in segregated services, on the lives of ordinary citizens, so that the rhythm of the days, weeks, seasons and life cycle would be made available to people in these settings and their rights upheld. These rights included the right to make choices and were not conditional upon behaving 'normally' or learning new skills.
>
> (Brown and Walmsley, 1997)

This approach did not tackle the issue of segregated services but focused on rights and equality in terms of quality of life. A more radical approach was to come from North America where Wolfensberger developed the concept further, attacking the way people with learning difficulties were seen as different from other people, often living in segregated institutions. He emphasised the importance of *integration* and minimising the differences between people.

> Central to his thinking, and subsequently to normalisation projects, is the imperative to integrate devalued people into the wider society and to ensure they adopt conventional social roles. This is crucial, he claims, if society is to have its social stereotypes about people with disabilities challenged and if people with disabilities themselves are to have opportunities to learn socially valued ways of behaving from 'valued' people and thereby break out of the negative roles to which they have been assigned (Szivos, 1992).

> Essentially, this means that people should be enabled to live, work and spend their leisure time in the same places and in the same fashion as non-disabled, ordinary people. The emphasis is on providing environments and activities which most ordinary citizens would want, and on presenting people with disabilities in ways which enhance their dignity and acceptability to others. This approach has seen people being offered services in ordinary houses, in small pseudo-family groups, and has led to

an emphasis on helping people find work, use ordinary facilities and draw
friends, acquaintances and sometimes advocates from the general public.

(Smith and Brown, 1992, p. 687)

In the UK the normalisation movement has had a strong influence on
the general trend towards de-institutionalisation and the provision of
care in the community. The work of groups such as the Campaign for
People with Mental Handicaps (O'Brien and Tyne, 1981; CMHP, 1984)
and the King's Fund Centre has been important in advocating this
approach. The King's Fund Centre document *An Ordinary Life* set out
what it described as 'comprehensive locally-based residential services'
(1980) and led to further work in areas such as employment (1984;
Towell, 1988). Primarily developed in relation to people with learning
difficulties the ideas have influenced work with other service users.

However, while the normalisation approach has been very influential it
also has its critics. Some have argued that by valuing 'normality' it can
place people with disability in a position where they are always
struggling to be 'normal' and often feeling inadequate. Disabled people
should value themselves and be valued as they are – not always striving
to be something else (Morris, 1991, 1993). Others have also pointed to
the limitation inherent in the concept of 'valued' people which fails to
recognise diversity based on age, sex, race, class and disability (Brown
and Smith, 1992).

4.2 Home and family as models for residential living

It is not surprising that a central model for normalising residential
services is the 'ordinary home'. In 1980, *An Ordinary Life* stated:

> *A residential service aims to provide a home and home-life for people who*
> *cannot find these independently. It makes it possible for people to live in a*
> *home of their own. A residential service is a home-making service. It uses*
> *two kinds of resources. The first are material – the buildings in which*
> *people live and the things they use to make them places of comfort,*
> *privacy and security. The second are even more important – the people*
> *who staff the service and bring to it their home-making skills. People who*
> *work as home-makers have two kinds of tasks – 'doing' and 'teaching'.*
> *They provide the settings and things which are needed to make a home*
> *and where necessary they do the tasks of daily living for the clients. Some*
> *of these tasks are very personal and private, others less so, but they are all*
> *part of what our society takes for granted as home-life. The people who*
> *work as home-makers also help their clients to provide for themselves*
> *what they need to make a home. They teach their clients to be more*
> *independent in the business of everyday life.*

(King's Fund Centre, 1980, p. 12)

In this quote the two elements of people and place are brought
together and the importance of home is stressed – a residential service is
a home-making service. The rhetoric of 'home' and 'family' has been
central in attempts to move away from institutional care. Yet as Unit 7
showed, home may not always be a haven. The idea of trying to recreate
a 'family group' is also seen in the terms 'home maker', 'house mother',
'house father' and home is often used by policy makers as an ideal or
model against which residential living can be measured. *Caring for People*,
the White Paper which accompanied the NHS and Community Care Act
1990, said that community care should 'enable people to live as normal a

life as possible in their own homes or in a homely environment in the community' (Department of Health, 1989, para 1.8). But the model is difficult to recreate.

In *An Ordinary Life* it was suggested that home could be:
- the person's parental home
- another family home
- a house with live-in staff
- a house without live-in staff.

Each of these types of home would need different forms of support and the authors suggested that this could be provided in a *core* and *cluster* system where 'one of the homes – usually slightly larger than the others – provides 'core services for the cluster' (King's Fund Centre, 1980, p. 19). This system was proposed as a comprehensive model and the principles are similar to developments which have taken place in services for children and people with mental health problems. But has the reality been so comprehensive? There has been a move away from hospital-based services for some groups of people to smaller settings based in the community. However, while the original authors of these plans may never have seen 'ordinary living' as a cheap alternative to institutional care, there have been criticisms that care in the community has in fact meant giving people less support – leaving them to cope on their own. The questions then become:
- are these genuinely 'homely' places?
- are they mini-institutions based in the community?

or
- are they accommodation without enough care?

Activity 12 Creating a 'homely domestic setting'

Allow about 10 minutes

In this activity, think about a small purpose-built group home for four to six adults with learning difficulties where people have their own rooms but their meals are shared and there is a live-in member of staff. Think about what kinds of things might make this setting feel home-like in the domestic sense of the word, and what things might make it feel like a small institution. Create two columns headed *Home-like* and *Institutional* and jot down ideas under each heading.

Comment

One of our course testers came up with this list:

Home-like	Institutional
Come and go as I please	Need for people to know where I am – 'booking-in' and 'booking-out' system
Friends/family to stay	Need to protect residents from 'exploitive' relationships
Make tea/coffee/meals when I choose	Doing things yourself may be difficult, dependent on abilities of individual
To have to clear up my own mess (but nobody else's)	Communal areas needing co-operative cleaning rotas
Buy own furniture/redecorate	Need for safe, approved fixtures and fittings
Manage own finances	Managing own finances may be difficult
To have my own front door key	Need for 'pass key'

By deliberately contrasting items this list highlights the fact that within a small group home issues of accountability, safety and risk-taking may lead to tensions between individual needs and groups needs. The environment may be more or less institutional depending on levels of support available and how they are used. There are parallels here with the discussion of arrangements for childminding in Unit 7.

Another issue for 'ordinary living' can be the way a scheme is accepted by the community. Some group schemes can be 'rejected by the neighbours' who voice their anxiety over the integration of people about whom they feel uncertain and the level of support they may receive.

Group living in large institutions

The rhetoric of family and home has also been applied to larger institutions (Higgins, 1989). In the 1970s when purpose-built local authority old people's homes were dominant, a building note was issued to architects which said that a home should be ' "domestic" as befits its function' (Department of Health and Social Security and Welsh Office, 1973, p. 5), and one way of doing this was to try and divide large institutional settings into smaller units.

> It was suggested that homes of between thirty and fifty places could be both economic and still allow for a certain level of domesticity: this would not be true of homes larger than fifty places. However, the Building Note also recommended the concept of 'group' or 'family' unit designs, saying 'units may provide the whole of the bedroom and sitting and dining space or may be confined to bedrooms with some or all of the

sitting space'. Groups could be used generally or to group together what were termed '"affinity" groups likely to be more compatible with each other than with other residents'. It was recommended that authorities should experiment with the concept.

(Peace, 1986, p. 143)

While new residential homes may often be built to a group unit design, creating compatible social groups may be almost impossible as a vacancy in a group usually has to be filled for financial reasons. Trying to manipulate an existing environment in order to create something more akin to a domestic home is also difficult. For many private homeowners offering residential and nursing home care to older people, it is their own home, often a large detached house, that becomes the residential home. For these homeowners, the importance now placed on providing single rooms can lead them to build modern extensions which may destroy something of the homely environment.

Some would say that trying to recreate a domestic environment out of a residential environment is impossible. Would it not be better if these varied alternative living arrangements stopped trying to be something they're not?

What do you think? Take a few minutes to reflect upon what you have learnt so far.

4.3 Collective living

The language of the 'home-like' environment in the literature on residential care reflects the way the family and family life are seen as the 'best' model of social organisation in our society (Dalley, 1996). But there are other models on which to base the organisation of daily living. Dalley, in *Ideologies of Caring*, contrasts the political ideologies of *individualism* (with its emphasis on the freedom of the individual) with *collectivism* (with its emphasis on social justice for all). She extends this argument to consider care and juxtaposes the sphere of family care, which has become private and individualised, with what she calls collective care based on *common values* and *shared responsibility* for *all members of society*. In developing collective care she shows how concerns over *public* provision in areas such as education, housing and health can be extended to the *private*, domestic sphere and discusses how feminists have both organised and written about collective alternatives to aspects of daily living traditionally the province of the family, for example day nurseries, public restaurants and central laundries.

Few suggestions have been made for the development of collective alternatives to the care of older people or people with disabilities. However, during the 1980s when feminist writing on caring took off (as we saw in Unit 1), Finch wrote in support of a residential alternative to family care:

> *On balance it seems to me that the residential route is the only one which ultimately will offer us the way out of the impasse of caring: collective solutions would, after all, be very much in the spirit of a socialist policy programme and a recognition that caring **is** labour, and in a wage economy should be paid as such, in principle should overcome some of the more offensive features of the various 'community' solutions.*

(Finch, 1984)

However, such suggestions have not found a great deal of support. While Finch was not advocating a form of institutionalised care, fears over institutionalisation have overshadowed the debate about developing collective living even though a number of religious and philanthropic organisations may define their own shared housing projects in a similar way (Cooper *et al.*, 1994).

Dalley, in trying to take forward these ideas, has outlined a number of principles for collective care which consider the needs of the individual within a group setting (1996, pp. 122–5). How do these ideas relate to the discussion so far about residential living and institutional care?

Activity 13   Principles of collective care

Allow about 10 minutes   Read through Dalley's principles of collective care below and decide whether you think any of the schemes we have discussed meet these principles.

- 'The first principle of collective care, which is also applicable to any form of care provision, must be for the disabled and/or dependent individual to be in a position to be responsible for his or her life choices. ... Equally, those who provide care should also be in a position to be responsible for decisions about their role in providing care.'

- 'The system of care should be responsive to the needs and inclinations of the individuals receiving care ... forms of care should be flexible in themselves – rigid routines and fixed expectations should play no part'.

- Maximal opportunity to form as wide and varied a range of personal relationships as the individual might wish.

- An equally maximal opportunity to develop skills and talents in any way that the individual chooses.

- A fifth principle should underwrite all the others: 'dependent people should be economically secure, to ensure that the other principles have real meaning.'

(1996, pp. 123–4)

Comment   It seems to me that the older people we heard from at Liberty of Earley House were experiencing a form of care which met these principles including the last one. Yet I feel that Liberty of Earley House appeals to those who want a form of individualised living. It is not a collective setting in terms of a shared commitment to common values and mutual support. It is also a segregated experience which does not display the community integration described in the black-led projects. Practice at Northenden Road also displayed many of these principles, while, as far as we can tell, it is difficult to see life at Cedar Court in this way. Perhaps, as was suggested earlier, the most important principle is the last, this is the issue of equal access to resources and financial security which enables people to make choices over where care is received.

When Dalley wrote the first edition of her book in 1988 she was criticised by people with disabilities (like Jenny Morris) for supporting a form of care which sought to exclude disabled people from society. More recently Dalley has offered a counter-argument suggesting that for some people 'memories of institutional care in the past preclude any consideration of new possibilities' and that the groups who form the focus of current community care policies are not homogeneous and that collective care may provide important alternative choices for some people (Dalley, 1996).

It seems to me that collective living as described here has moved away from the earlier notion of 'collective' as a truly shared experience to one which recognises the tensions for individuals living in groups and stresses equality of opportunity.

4.4 Residential living — has it changed?

Over the past 20 years enormous changes have taken place in the provision of accommodation and care for people who, for whatever reason, do not live within domestic settings. While there has been a general decline in institutional and residential care for some groups such as children, there has also been a growth in community-based residential schemes and, in particular, settings offering long-term care to frail older people. Some of the factors affecting this demand are given in the box below.

Factors which may affect the demand for long-term care for older people

- Demographic: increase in the number of very old people; increased morbidity with increasing age; in particular, increase in numbers of older people suffering from dementing illnesses.

- Social: changes in the pattern of family structures and responsibilities at work and at home; increased tendency for some families to live at a distance from each other.

- Economic/consumer: improved financial position of many older people; older people making a positive choice over long-term care.

- Service: increased pressure on long-stay hospital beds; more effective use of acute hospital beds; closure of psychiatric hospitals.

- Political: initial stimulation through public funding of private and voluntary provision via supplementary benefit; community care legislation; attack on residential provision. Transfer of state funding to cash-limited local authority budgets since April 1993.

- Ideological: increasing popular support for a pluralist approach to welfare during the 1980s. Increasing reliance during the late 1980s and 1990s on the market within health and social welfare services.

(Peace et al., 1997, p. 23)

These changes have led to a diversity in the providers of care and the settings of care and ongoing concern for the quality of care and the quality of life provided. In the case of provision for older people some of these changes are reflected in *A Better Home Life*, a new code of practice for residential care homes which updates *Home Life* (Centre for Policy on Ageing, 1984, 1996).

Activity 14   **A better home life**

Allow about 10 minutes

Listen again to Audio Cassette 2, side 2. The final comments are made by Kina, Lady Avebury, Chair of the working group responsible for the new code of practice for residential care for older people *A Better Home Life* (Centre for Policy on Ageing, 1996). As you listen make a note of the reasons she gives for developing a new code of practice, those things which are new to the code and those areas which are still undeveloped.

Comment

The change from a generic document *(Home Life)* to a code centred on the lives of older people is indicative of the continuing importance of residential settings which offer accommodation and care to very old people. *A Better Home Life* covers a range of accommodation and care – from sheltered housing to nursing homes.

In the interview Kina Avebury says that the new code:

- recognises advances in design but acknowledges the difficult economic circumstances in which many homeowners operate

- highlights issues of caring for people with dementia

- acknowledges the need for family members to have a role in residential care

- recognises that further attention needs to be paid to issues for minority ethnic groups

- is not prescriptive about staffing levels as the range of facilities discussed is too great.

Many of those who work in care settings feel that practice has improved and that there has been a general raising of standards. Yet, the scandals of bad practice still emerge. Issues of resourcing are ever present, and there is always the feeling that within closed environments institutionalisation may be a convenient form of care and abuse may be waiting to happen. Residential living may always be vulnerable to such abuse, yet we have also seen that fulfilment is possible in living arrangements other than the family.

Key points

- The principles of normalisation were developed to counter the trends towards institutionalisation. They stressed integration and conformity with what are seen as dominant values in society.

- Critiques of normalisation have questioned the societal values on which it is based.

- The rhetoric of home and family is dominant in discussion around 'ordinary living'.

- Some authors have challenged this dominance of the family and offered an alternative model of collective care.

Section 5
Regulation

5.1 Why regulate?

While local authority homes were the major form of residential provision up until the late 1970s, they were not registered and inspected in the same way as the private and voluntary sectors (independent sector). Instead they were subject to internal review. However, following the dramatic growth of privatised services in the early 1980s, the Registered Homes Act 1984 consolidated a detailed system of regulation (registration and inspection) for independent sector residential care and nursing homes, and the reforms of the NHS and Community Care Act 1990 brought public sector services into this system. The development of these legal frameworks is given in Care in the UK. Look at this now and refer to it during the course.

These changes in residential provision have led the state to move from being a provider to a state which purchases and regulates. But is regulation necessary?

Activity 15 **Why regulate care settings?**

Allow about 10 minutes What reasons might be given for regulating residential care settings? Try to note down at least two reasons.

Comment The first thing that probably came into your mind was a need to protect people from poor standards of care. People seeking residential care may be vulnerable to abuse, they may be looking for a 'home for life' and may not have the resources to 'shop around'. You may also have thought that all care homes should be of a 'certain standard' and that this might improve people's quality of life. Regulation may also counter the closed nature of the institution opening it up to the outside world.

However, standards are not the same as quality. Standard setting can be seen as 'minimalist regulation' concerned with avoiding risk rather than enhancing quality.

In a study of the regulation of residential care for older people, Day and her colleagues (1996) give these reasons for moving beyond minimalist regulation:

- Provision can change rapidly, for example a home may go out of business or change hands, so people need protection against change. Therefore regulation needs to be an ongoing process.

- The public sector is still a provider of services and so public accountability for public spending is still important, as is wider public accountability for public policy.

Many of the issues raised here apply to all of the various care settings we have covered in this block. Whether or not people are spending short or long periods of time within a care setting which is not their own home, or whether they are receiving a service within their own home, there should be a system which seeks to monitor standards, enhance quality and protect people from abuse. (The issue of abuse forms the focus of Block 6.)

While some of these issues can be covered in the contracts set up between purchasers and providers (which were discussed in Unit 3), they only apply to those people who are in some way publicly funded and so those who purchase care directly are not protected. This is another reason for regulation.

But there are other views on regulation. Some independent sector providers feel that as local authorities are allowed to set their own standards within the basic legal framework, variation can only be ruled out by having a national inspectorate or by allowing the independent sector to set its own standards through its own professional bodies. In 1997 the Burgner review of regulation and inspection of social services recommended that inspection units might be moved to local authority trading standards departments (Burgner, 1996). A debate is ensuing about whether regulation should be offered at a national or local level.

Today, a local authority inspection unit might be responsible for a wide range of settings and services and yet there are enormous variations between units in terms of personnel and other resources. The following box gives an example of the range of responsibilities carried out by what is termed a medium-sized inspection unit and the number of facilities under its remit. As we saw in Unit 3, currently regulation is not mandatory in relation to home care services, although many authorities operate voluntary accreditation schemes. The signs are that in future domiciliary care services will be regulated.

Responsibilities of a medium-sized inspection unit

Residential homes for adults (elderly, elderly mental infirm, mental health, learning disabilities, physical disabilities, substance abuse)

Private	84
Voluntary	28
Local authority	30
Total	*142*

Residential homes for three or fewer adults (elderly, mental health, learning disabilities, physical disabilities)

Private	10
Voluntary	18
Local authority	26
Total	*54*

Day-care facilities for children under eight

Childminders	386
Playgroups	119
Day nurseries	25
Nursery schools	2
Out of school	22
Open access	28
Creches	10
Family centres (LA only)	6
Total	*598*

Facilities for children

Children's homes	7
Non-maintained special schools	1
Boarding schools	1
Total	9

Voluntary registration of domiciliary and day care services

Private domiciliary	3
Voluntary domiciliary	1
Private day care	1
Total	5

Investigation of complaints

(Day et al., 1996, p. 13)

Inspection units run by health authorities are responsible for inspecting nursing homes and some private hospitals and clinics.

5.2 Accountability

The final part of this unit looks in more detail at being held to account, a central issue for regulation, and returns to Liberty of Earley House which, like all residential care homes, is registered and inspected under the Registered Homes Act 1984.

When the care manager, Ann Hamilton, was asked if being registered under the Registered Homes Act made any difference to her work she commented:

> *I think it just makes you aware of everything that you need legally to provide ... it covers a multitude of things, mostly form filling and reports, we have to record accidents, any medication given, we have to provide regular fire checks and fire drills, maintain all equipment, work under the Health and Safety Act, COSHH policies – control of substances hazardous to health, and just basically maintain the safety and security of everybody in the home, and we have bi-annual inspections by the quality assurance team from social services.*

When asked whether all this activity affected the lives of residents she carried on:

> *We don't really find it interferes with anything. The formal things we have to do are kept separate, but the home's run for residents, and that doesn't interfere with it at all.*

Ann's viewpoint is one that sees the procedures of regulation as very much her business. As far as possible she does not want these processes to impinge upon the way in which residents wish to live their lives. But of course, these rules and regulations do affect the way people can live in group settings. Think back to Maurice Heather's comments about the design of the lounge on the ground floor:

> *It's quite apparent now that the home hasn't got a large space where all the residents can gather together for a special occasion, and I think if we'd wrestled with the fire officer rather harder we might have found a way of opening up the ground floor lounge and dining room with the reception,*

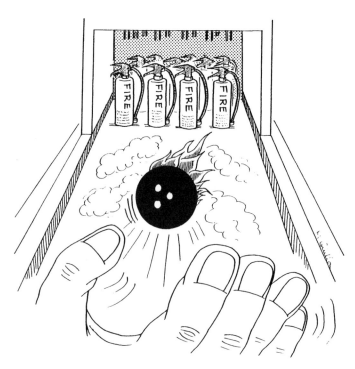

There's no playing with fire

so on occasions that could have been flung open for a large party or a reception, and I also gather they would quite like to play indoor bowls which they can't do at the moment. The means of escape requirements would have to be compromised if the lounge/dining room had opened into the reception area because the reception area is a continuation of the means of escape and as it is we've got a door between the two spaces which are on hold-open devices, so in a sense you have a flow between them but you can't actually hold a party or a gathering very successfully.

Hold-open devices are used in many homes where heavy fire doors impede mobility for some residents but here they haven't proved a perfect solution.

Issues of design may seem of minor importance compared to other aspects of accountability, although the physical environment can be used to reinforce aspects of the organisation. A tension can develop between the needs of an organisation to be publicly accountable, and the needs of individuals to continue to take risks and be responsible for themselves. Residents should be aware that the place they live in is regulated and the implications this may have for their lives. They should also be aware of the procedures for inspection and how they could make an input if they wished.

Activity 16   **Regulated lives**

Allow about 15 minutes   In the Offprints Book you will find an extract from the annual inspection
    report for Liberty of Earley House undertaken in February 1995 (Offprint 12). Read the extract and consider the position of the residents, staff and inspectors over the issue of accidents. Think back to the audio cassette to what the staff said about risk assessment and the alarm system, and to residents' comments about self-care. You may wish to listen to part of the tape again, especially the comments by residents and staff. What do you think being accountable might mean for each of these groups?

Comment   Concern about accidents raises a number of issues about accountability.

For residents. Within the privacy of their own flats they cannot be seen but having a pendant alarm does enable them to make contact with staff (Freda's experience on the tape). There is a trade-off between privacy, autonomy and safety, and yet residents still take responsibility for their actions. In this respect they are accountable for themselves.

For staff. Given the nature of the environment they cannot survey residents as a group except at mealtimes or on special occasions, although staff commented that all residents are seen on each shift and some residents are checked more often than others. They record all incidents in order to be accountable for residents' actions. Carrying out risk assessments and reviewing on a regular basis also maximises safety.

For inspectors. Inspectors wish to improve on record keeping as a means by which the staff (and the organisation) are accountable for the actions of residents and have something in writing which could be used should a dispute occur.

An increase in accidents may be seen as an indicator of poor practice by inspectors but a consequence of resident autonomy by others.

We will be looking more closely at accountability and keeping records in Block 5.

At this point you might like to stop and think about the inspection process. Inspectors have to go into a care home at least twice a year, and one inspection is usually unannounced. They commonly spend a day in the home and will divide their time between inspecting records, observing, and talking with staff and residents. They will look around the public areas and talk to some people within their own private rooms. In recent years lay-inspectors have become part of inspection teams and if there is more than one person inspecting, then the team can divide its tasks with some people spending more time talking to residents.

 In the Offprint article about Northenden Road, Paul Newton acted as a lay inspector and gave his snapshot view of the unit. Obviously, a lot of preparatory work is carried out before inspections take place but you might want to take another look at his one-day assessment, consider what kind of picture is painted by his overall ratings and compare it with the discussion of this scheme in the text.

Key points

- Regulation through registration and inspection can be seen as a way of providing a check on standards in care settings. The present system focuses on standards of provision rather than quality of care or quality of life.

- Some providers in the independent sector favour a national inspectorate to overcome variations in standards across the country, or regulation through professional bodies.

- Accountability is a key aspect of regulation and may be experienced differently by residents, staff and inspectors.

- Inspections provide a snapshot view of a home or unit at one point in time.

Conclusion

This unit began by looking at Liberty of Earley House as an example of a person-centred approach to residential living where residents experience accommodation of a high standard and maintain control over their lives through negotiated care. This form of living contrasts dramatically with institutionalised care where the power of the individual has been lost, quality of life is poor and the organisation dominates. In exploring care for older people we saw that both forms of care co-exist and those most likely to experience institutional care are the least powerful, least well-off and most unsupported.

Looking at the experiences of children in care and black perspectives of residential care confirmed some of the aspects of good practice seen with older people. A concern for the whole person is crucial and both keyworking and care planning are mentioned in all settings. Northenden Road brought the issues of rights to the fore, while the black-led projects demonstrated a wider meaning of community integration and how the experience and understanding of racism can become central to a holistic philosophy of care.

These examples have shown how residential care can be developed into a positive form of accommodation and care. But the power of institutionalisation is strong and a counter attack has been led by ideas of normalisation, and the model of home and family. Trying to model living arrangements, daily relationships and activities as close to family life as possible is a problem if you aren't a family and cannot possibly recreate its central dynamics. At its best, then, residential living may combine independence with security, and because it is run by one group of people for another standards need to be regulated. Yet accountability is bound to place different sets of demands on settings whose main function should be to enhance quality of life through the provision of accommodation and care.

In the final unit of this block we return to various points in Units 6, 7 and 8 and explore in further detail practice skills concerned with moving between settings and care planning, and study skills relating to understanding numbers.

> **Study skills: Studying with a group**
> We have been talking about group living in this unit, but what about group studying? Have you be able to get to the K100 tutorials, or make other kinds of contact with fellow students? What are you supposed to get out of tutorials anyway? Are they worth the time and expense? Could you be learning more at home? And what about day schools or self-help study meetings? Some people manage perfectly well studying on their own. Others swear that they would never have coped without the camaraderie and support they gained from other students and the wise words of their tutor. Which is right for you? To help you think about these questions once more before you get too far into the course, read *The Good Study Guide*, Chapter 3, Sections 1 and 2. You have already read some of this so it will be quite an easy read.

References

Baldwin, N., Harris, J. and Kelly, D. (1993) 'Institutionalisation: why blame the institution?', *Ageing and Society*, Vol. 13, No. 1, pp. 69–81.

Barton, R. (1959) *Institutional Neurosis*, John Wright, Bristol.

Brown, H. and Smith, H. (1992) 'Assertion, not assimilation: a feminist perspective on the normalisation principle', in Brown, H. and Smith, H. (eds) *Normalisation: A Reader for the Nineties*, Routledge, London.

Brown, H. and Walmsley, J. (1997) 'When "ordinary" isn't enough: a review of the concept of normalisation', in Bornat, J., Johnson, J., Pereira, C., Pilgrim, D. and Williams, F. (eds) *Community Care: A Reader*, Macmillan in association with the Open University, London.

Burgner, T. (1996) *The Regulation and Inspection of Social Services*, Department of Health and Welsh Office, HMSO, London.

Centre for Policy on Ageing (1984) *Home Life: A Code of Practice for Residential Care*, Centre for Policy on Ageing, London.

Centre for Policy on Ageing (1996) *A Better Home Life*, Centre for Policy on Ageing, London.

CMHP (1984) *Hope for the Future? CMHPs Evidence to the Social Services Committee on Community Care*, Campaign for Mentally Handicapped People, London.

Cooper, R., Watson, L. and Allan, G. (1994) *Shared Living: Social Relations in Supported Housing*, Social Services Monograph: Research in Practice, University of Sheffield: Joint Unit for Social Services, Research and Community Care.

Dalley, G. (1996) *Ideologies of Caring: Rethinking Community and Collectivism*, Macmillan Educational Books, Basingstoke.

Day, P., Klein, R. and Redmayne, S. (1996) *Why Regulate?*, The Policy Press, Bristol.

Department of Health (1989) *Caring for People: Community Care in the Next Decade and Beyond*, Cm 849, HMSO, London.

Department of Health and Social Security and Welsh Office (1973) *Local Authority Building Note No. 2: Residential Accommodation for Elderly People*, HMSO, London.

Emerson, E. (1992) 'What is normalisation?', in Brown, H. and Smith, H. (eds) *Normalisation: A Reader for the Nineties*, Routledge, London.

Finch, J. (1984) 'Community care: developing non-sexist alternatives', *Critical Social Policy*, Vol. 3, No. 9, pp. 6–18.

Gavilan, H. (1992) 'Care in the community: issues of dependency and control – the similarities between institution and home', *Generations Review*, Vol. 2, No. 4, pp. 9–11.

Goffman, E. (1961) *Asylums*, Penguin Books, London.

Higgins, J. (1989) 'Home and institution', in Allen, G. and Crow, G. (eds) *Home and Family: Creating the Domestic Sphere*, Macmillan, London.

Jones, K. and Fowles, A.J. (1984) *Ideas on Institutions: Analysing the Literature on Long Term Care and Custody*, Routledge and Kegan Paul, London.

King, R.D., Raynes, N. and Tizard, J. (1971) *Patterns of Residential Care*, Routledge and Kegan Paul, London.

King's Fund Centre (1980) *An Ordinary Life: Comprehensive Locally-based Residential Services for Mentally Handicapped People*, King's Fund Centre, London.

King's Fund Centre, (1984) *An Ordinary Working Life: Vocational Services for People with Mental Handicap*, King's Fund Centre, London.

Laing, W. (1996) *Laing's Review of Private Healthcare 1996*, Laing and Buisson Publications, London.

Lansbury, G. (1928) *My Life*, Constable and Co., London.

Morris, J. (1991) *Pride Against Prejudice: Transforming Attitudes to Disability*, The Women's Press, London.

Morris, J. (1993) *Independent Lives: Community Care and Disabled People*, Macmillan, London.

NISW (National Institute for Social Work) (1988a) *Residential Care: A Positive Choice*, HMSO, London.

NISW (National Institute for Social Work) (1988b) *Residential Care: The Research Reviewed*, HMSO, London.

NISW (National Institute for Social Work) (1993) *Residential Care: Positive Answers*, HMSO, London.

Opit, L. and Pahl, J. (1993) 'Institutional care for elderly people: can we predict admissions?', *Research, Policy and Planning*, Vol. 10, No. 2, pp. 2–5.

Peace, S. (1986) 'The Design of Residential Homes: an historical perspective', in Judge, K. and Sinclair, I. (eds) *Residential Care for Elderly People*, HMSO, London.

Peace, S., Kellaher, L. and Willcocks, D. (1982) *A Balanced Life? A Consumer Study of Residential Life in 100 Local Authority Old People's Homes*, Research Report No. 14, Social Research Unit, Polytechnic of North London.

Peace, S., Kellaher, L. and Willcocks, D. (1997) *Re-evaluating Residential Care*, Open University Press, Buckingham.

Residential Forum (1996) *Creating a Home from Home: A Guide to Standards*, National Institute for Social Work, London.

Smith, H. and Brown, H. (1992) 'Defending community care: can normalization do the same job?' *British Journal of Social Work*, Vol. 22, No. 6, pp. 658–93.

Szivos, S. (1992) 'The limits to integration?', in Brown, H. and Smith, H. (eds) *Normalisation: A Reader for the Nineties*, Routledge, London.

Thompson, P., Itzin, C. and Abendstern, M. (1990) *I Don't Feel Old: Understanding the Experience of Later Life*, Oxford University Press, Oxford.

Towell, D. (1988) *An Ordinary Life in Practice*, King's Fund Centre, London.

Townsend, P. (1962) *The Last Refuge*, Routledge and Kegan Paul, London.

White, D. (1994) *On Being the Relative of Someone in a Home*, The Relatives' Association, London.

Willcocks, D., Peace, S. and Kellaher, L. (1987) *Private Lives in Public Places*, Tavistock Publications, London.

Women's Design Service (1991) *Designing Housing for Older Women*, Women's Design Service, London.

Youll, P.J. and McCourt-Perring, C. (1993) *Raising Voices: Ensuring Quality in Residential Care*, HMSO, London.

Acknowledgements

Grateful acknowledgement is made to the following sources for permission to reproduce material in this unit:

Text

p.138/9: Day, P., Klein, R. and Redmayne, S. (1996) *Why Regulate?*, p.13, The Polity Press.

Illustrations

p. 104/5: Achitects' drawings of Liberty of Earley House, © P R P Architects; *p. 112*: Centre for Policy on Ageing/HMSO, crown copyright is reproduced with the permission of the Controller of Her Majesty's Stationery Office; *p. 114*: courtesy of Emeritus Professor Peter Townsend; *p. 121*: Sally and Richard Greenhill; *p. 123*: Neil O'Connor; *p. 125*: Bob Watkins/Photofusion.

Unit 9
Supporting People in Changing Circumstances

Prepared for the course team by Sheila Peace

While you are working on Unit 9, you will need:
- Offprints Book
- *The Good Study Guide*
- Media Notes
- Skills video

Contents

Introduction

Unit 9 focuses on:

- making a move
- planning life in a care setting
- working with numbers
- developing writing skills.

This is the second of the K100 skills units as outlined in Unit 5. There, we said that these units are designed to develop your practice skills by helping you:

- reflect on what you can do

- acknowledge the skills you possess

- describe your skills in words in such a way as to demonstrate their transferability to a wide range of situations.

To do this you began by considering some of the principles which should underpin good practice in social care and you developed new skills through observation of practice using the skills video, some of which you recorded for future use. This unit uses a similar format to explore practice skills which link directly to the work you have done in Block 2. We also continue to look in more detail at the study skills involved in working with numbers.

Central themes of the unit

This block has focused on the context in which care takes place and the way the environment of care can affect care relationships. Stop and think for a moment about the wide variety of places you have considered and the knowledge you have gained. If you think about this in terms of theories and ideas, policy and practice, then you might summarise the knowledge base of the block in this way:

- knowledge about *theories and ideas* – Goffman's ideas on total institutions and institutionalisation; feminist perspectives on women and the home; the concepts of public and private space; ideas about attachment to place and relocation

- knowledge about *policy* – 'special needs' housing; the Wagner review of residential care; the regulation of care settings

- knowledge about *practice* – joint working in relation to housing and care services; how people use space in care settings – issues of privacy and access; support for people who are moving; care planning and keyworking; developing a philosophy of care in residential services.

By reflecting on the knowledge you have gained in the block you can see how to make connections with practice and practice skills. In fact there is a lot of material here that could be used and I will have to be selective.

Given that the focus of the block has been on the way people interact with their environment, often changing places in order to receive care, the focus here is on two common experiences:

- making a move
- planning life in a care setting.

The aim will be to look at the role of the care worker within these areas of practice and the skills needed to facilitate that role. However, moving between places is a common experience for many people, so even if you are not directly involved in care work, the reflections here may have wider benefits.

While a number of skills will be identified, the main focus of this unit will be around planning and support. In addition, further consideration will be given to the principles of good practice outlined in Unit 5 and special attention will be paid to the first of these:

- enable people to develop their own potential.

As in Unit 5, the K100 skills video will form the main medium through which practice is observed. In this unit you will look at three short video scenes which follow on from those you viewed in Unit 5.

Unit 9 video content

Scene 4 'No time for goodbyes': a young boy living in a short-term assessment unit is told by his keyworker that he will be moving shortly to live with a foster family.

Scene 5 'The visit': a young boy and his social worker visit the foster family with whom he is to be placed, in their home.

Scene 6 'Getting to know you': an older person and her key worker in a residential care home discuss managing medication.

Finally, if you are interested in taking a Vocational Qualification in Care you will find that some of the work you do here will be of value in relation to practice with people who are making changes in their lives. For further information on mapping the VQ areas see the Pathways VQ Guide.

Section 1
Making a move

Most people will have moved at some point in their lives and even if
you have not moved yourself, then you probably know someone who
has. Moving can be stressful and how people cope often has a lot to do
with who is there to help.

Activity 1   **Help with moving**

Allow about 10 minutes   When asked what aspects of moving she found difficult, a friend gave the
following list. Consider each of the points she made and note in the right-
hand column what you think might help to alleviate these difficulties.

Difficulties	What would help?
The actual planning of it all, it was exhausting	Planning over a period of time, lists, assistance
Leaving somewhere that held a lot of memories, saying goodbye	Help + support, time to say goodbye. Taking photos,
Not being able to take everything with me and having to get rid of things	Picking our 'special' things and careful planning new space. Organising where things should go.
Being worried that it's going to be the wrong move or that it might all fall through	Clear about options, discuss all eventuality with adviser.
Everything being unfamiliar: it made me feel insecure	Making new environment as friendly and homely as soon as possible. Be prepared to feel 'new' and to come to terms with change.

Comment   I thought of the following:

Difficulties	What would help?
The actual planning of it all, it was exhausting	Planning in advance and trying to be organised. Having enough people around. Food and drink.
Leaving somewhere that held a lot of memories, saying goodbye	Having someone with me when moving, but also time alone to say my own goodbyes. Take photos.
Not being able to take everything with me and having to get rid of things	Planning what I want to take. Organising getting rid of things. Making decisions over what to throw away and what to give away (I might need help with this).
Being worried that it's going to be the wrong move or that it might all fall through	Having someone to talk to about moving. Being as well informed as I can about where I am going and what might happen if I can't move. Knowing my options.
Everything being unfamiliar: it made me feel insecure	Recognising that it might take time to adjust to a new place and new people. Being prepared to feel a bit sad.

These comments begin to tell us that some of the things people value when moving are:

- planning in advance and organising the move
- having information about where you are moving to and what the options are
- on the day having someone with you
- having some time on your own to say goodbye.

If you think back over Block 2 you have met a number of people such as Joan Price and Esther Hurdle, who have moved between places in order to meet their care needs, and for some of them the transitions between places have not been so smooth or planned or timely. Joan Price, who moved into Liberty of Earley House, gave this account of her move:

Joan, making her new home

I had such a very short time to get any impressions, I looked around on the Tuesday of one week, and then Mrs Hamilton phoned me on the Monday of the following week and said they'd had a cancellation and would I be able to take it, so really I didn't have time except that when I looked round I was impressed and thought it did seem very nice, and my cousin who came with me had been a social worker and she was very impressed and she said if I'm impressed it must be alright ...

Well really my first day here was a complete muddle because I had so much stuff that we had to unpack, and boxes to clear and for the first few days really it was just a question of stowing things away and finding somewhere to put things and I'd lived in a bungalow on my own for years, and had it all to myself and then to cram everything that I'd brought into the space available here, although it is adequate you know it was difficult. But other than that everything seemed to be alright.

Esther Hurdle moved from:

- home to hospital
- between hospitals, and
- from hospital to home.

During the course of this time she had to come to terms with using a wheelchair and her final move was to accessible housing. This happened over a period of years. If you think about it, Esther had to live without many possessions in unfamiliar environments for several years, only coming home at weekends. Esther's story demonstrates a number of important points about moving for people with physical disabilities, in particular that both the physical environment and personal assistance are important.

Use your knowledge to think about planning a move into a care setting, for example a residential home or hostel. It may be helpful to have a quick look back at Section 3 of Unit 7 to remind yourself of some of the issues raised about transitions and change. You will be doing some more work on planning a move in Activity 5. For many of the people featured in this block being informed about change has been particularly important and we have already identified being informed as an essential part of all moves. So what kind of information helps?

Activity 2 **Information that helps**

Allow about 10 minutes Put yourself in the shoes of someone who is making a move to a residential home. What information would you need to help you make this move? Try and answer the following questions:

(a) What would you want to know about the place?

(b) What would be a good way of being given this information?

Comment Here are some of the points you might have thought about:

(a) There are lots of questions I'd want answered. These are just some of them.

- Where is the home; how far is it from where I live now?
- What does it look like; what facilities does it have?
- Is it near the shops, doctors etc?
- Is there a bus to the nearby town?
- How many people live there – residents and staff?
- Will I have my own room?

- What can I bring with me – furniture etc? Can I store anything?
- I have a cat, will I have to get rid of him?
- What is the routine like, are there rules?
- If I need help with medication what would happen?
- If this fell through what are the other options?
- What is it all going to cost and how will I pay for it?

(b)   Well, if I was in touch with a social worker or care manager I'd expect them to know some of these things. But a family member might also have gathered some information. There may also be a brochure or some written material. But most of all I'd want to go and see the place for myself. A visit would be important.

The questions seem endless, but then moving from one place to another is a very important transition. It means up-rooting yourself and everything that has meaning to you and taking it somewhere else.

What this activity has done is shown us the importance of having information. Anyone who supports someone else through a move will seek information. You have probably done this yourself. But how do you find the information you need? If you wanted to help an older relative find out about residential care you might start by ringing the social services department who then tell you to contact your local Registration and Inspection Unit for a list of registered residential care homes in your area. The list may at least be a starting point for approaching homes and they may send you a brochure. Finding out information for ourselves may not always be easy but as a care worker being informed and being skilled in giving information becomes part of the job. The next activity looks at being an informed care worker.

Activity 3   Being informed and giving information

Allow about 10 minutes   In order to help someone else you need to be informed yourself. If you were a care worker helping an older person make a move to residential care, how would you go about gaining information and how would you pass it on?

In particular, think about what you would do if the person you were helping had specific cultural or religious needs?

Write down how you would go about it and then make a list of what skills you have used.

Comment   As as care worker helping someone with a move you would probably know something about the home they were moving to or the range of options available. But you may not have visited the homes yourself and your knowledge may be out of date. You may just be working from a list. If I was in this position I would want to find out more myself so that I could pass on accurate information. This would mean liaising with other people from a range of agencies and obtaining written information where possible that you could pass on.

Also I'd want to be clear on certain aspects of information that I know will be important, such as financial arrangements and facilities, and whether or not people can have a room of their own. Having the time to do all these things may be a problem and you may not be able to do all the visits you'd like, so knowing the 'right' people to ask will also be important.

There may be specific cultural or ethnic groups that you should talk to who run schemes outside mainstream provision, for example schemes like the black-led residential homes you read about in Unit 8 that were run by voluntary organisations. I would want to visit places myself and try to assess the advantages and disadvantages of different schemes.

A number of skills around information have been mentioned here:

- liaising with other agencies
- obtaining written material
- gathering information through visits
- being informed on key facts such as finance and facilities.

If you stop and think about it for a moment the skills listed here are commonly used by most people when they move house, except then it's the estate agent and the buyers and sellers who provide the information. Having information is just one part of the process of planning a move; to look at some other aspects of that process we are going to use the skills video. Here we want you to observe practice, record your observations and then consider your own practice within a similar situation. The first video scenario looks at issues around leave taking.

This sequence centres on Lloyd and his keyworker, Fran. Lloyd is a black African-Caribbean child. He is 13 years old and currently living in a short-term assessment unit (rather like Northenden Road which you read about in Unit 7). He has been there five months and is waiting to be placed with a black foster family which has been organised through his social worker, Maggie. He has become very friendly with one of the other boys at the unit called Louis, who is away for a few days.

Activity 4   Video scene 4 'No time for goodbyes'

Allow about 30 minutes

Play scene 4. Now rewind and play it again. This time make some notes about the way this move is being handled. Here are some questions to get you started.

- Does this move seem planned?
- Does Lloyd have enough information?
- What are the concerns of the worker?
- What are Lloyd's concerns?
- Does the way the worker handles this news seem likely to enhance Lloyd's self-esteem or undermine his confidence?

Try to explain the reasons for your views.

Comment   While Lloyd has known for some time that he is going to move to live with a foster family, he isn't prepared to move so quickly. In this scenario the move seems very unplanned. He is unprepared for this news. He met the

Lloyd and Fran

family a month ago and feels uncertain. Note his thoughts: 'How does she know I like them, I only met them once'.

The information Fran is giving is second hand, from Maggie, Lloyd's social worker, and it comes across as hurried and fragmented. Lloyd is left with very little information about what is going to happen to him and how the actual move is going to be organised on the day. He knows that he is moving shortly and will have to pack all his things. He does not know who will help him or who will go with him.

Fran seems more concerned with the fact that the move will go ahead than with how Lloyd feels. She barely listens to his responses. You can hear this in the way she says 'Brilliant, isn't it! After all this time at last we've got somewhere!' She is rushed and does not take time to talk things through; she will not even be around on the day of the move.

Lloyd is left feeling bewildered, overwhelmed and concerned that his friend Louis is not around at the moment and that he won't be able to say goodbye to him. He's feeling sad and will not even have a familiar member of unit staff to help him – only Don, whom he doesn't think much of: 'that prat'. I thought this wasn't handled very well at all and that Lloyd might be feeling very anxious about the whole thing.

I think you will agree that the practice observed here is not as good as it could be. Some of the observations can be summarised in the following way:

- unplanned move, poor advance planning and preparation
- unexplained move
- no proper time for goodbyes
- lack of continuity over who is involved
- rushed move leaves no one time to think
- lack of information and understanding of the person's needs. This might lead to unfulfilled expectations on all sides and breakdown.

While this scenario does not seem like a situation caused by a crisis, responding to crisis is common so we could add to this list:

- having to do something in a crisis (often called 'crisis intervention') can lead to poor planning.

The issues raised here have been commented on in research into children leaving care homes and moving to foster families or leaving care settings altogether to begin living independently. Some children in these circumstances make lots of unexplained moves. In the Offprints Book you will find the 'Social Services Inspectorate Standards for leaving care' (Offprint 13) which reinforces some of these points. You may like to look at it now.

Activity 5   **Planning a move**

Allow about 20 minutes

Now it's your turn. If you were Lloyd's social worker how would you plan Lloyd's move to live with a foster family? This activity is in two parts: part (a) looks at planning a move and part (b) looks at the skills involved.

(a)   Planning a move

Think through the process of moving. Begin from the point where an assessment has already been carried out and a decision taken to move. Map out what you think would be the important stages and any particular issues involved in each stage. For example, the first stage might be to 'talk about the idea of moving'.

If you are a practitioner in a different situation to Fran or Maggie you may wish to map out a plan for someone you work with, for example an older person moving into residential care, a person with learning difficulties or mental health problems moving into a hostel, or a young person leaving care altogether.

Write your responses in the box provided, concentrating on the first two columns.

Planning a move

Stages in the process	Notes on stages	Skills
Talk about the idea of moving	Get Lloyd used to the idea	

Allow about 10 minutes   (b)   Skills involved

Now look down the list of stages and any notes you have made and write into the third column the skills you would use in relation to each stage.

Comment (to parts (a) and (b))   You may wish to compare your plan with the one I have outlined below.

Planning a move

Stages in the process	Notes on stages	Skills
Talk about the idea of moving	Get Lloyd used to the idea	Listening, communicating information giving, practical and emotional support, recording
Find the right place to move to even if it takes time	Focus on needs of individual	Networking, communicating, negotiating, planning
Give information	Make sure information in accessible form – print, braille, etc.	Communicating, listening, facilitating access
Make visit or visits	Make sure these are planned and people have information in advance	Planning, organising, facilitating, supporting, informing
Prepare plan for the move	Plan packing, transport, who's going to be there, how the day will proceed	Organising, facilitating, supporting
Leave taking, saying goodbyes	Allow time. Facilitate photos if wished or other ways of marking the event, e.g. good luck cards, gifts. Think about who should be involved	Supporting, enabling, listening, networking
Settling in/making the transition	Importance of possessions. Memories from the past. It's a gradual process, can't be rushed	Supporting, enabling, listening, planning, communicating, recording
Monitor progress	Consider how person is adjusting to new situation. What else needs to be done?	Monitoring, planning, recording, assessing, negotiating, listening, supporting

Photocopy your work from this activity and keep it in your K100 portfolio. If you decide to do an NVQ in care, this type of material may provide useful evidence.

As we can see from this list the whole process of moving between settings can be complex; the very nature of the situation and the people and places involved mean that while the sequence of events may have a similar pattern there will always be individual variations. There are also a wide range of skills involved and I expect you came up with some I haven't mentioned.

While this activity has focused on planning, you can see that a key aspect of the process is supporting someone through a period of adjustment. At this point look back at Hopson and Adams's model of changes in self-esteem during transition given in Unit 7, Section 3.3 and think about how your plan might incorporate support for someone undergoing such change.

One aspect of moving on most people's lists will be making a visit. People buying a new house or flat do this all the time. In that situation the estate agent provides the information and may accompany people but prospective buyers will have their list of requirements. However, moving into or between care settings is different. Here we are involved with people and places and a two-way visit is common. The individual visits their new 'home', while staff or foster family members may also visit the person in their current setting. The purpose of making a visit is multiple. It is an occasion for the person moving to see their new environment and meet some of the people with whom they are going to live. In the case of a young person moving in with a foster family it may be the first opportunity to meet all the family members; this will be a different situation from that of an older person moving into a residential home but there are some similarities.

The next activity focuses on a visit Lloyd and Maggie make to meet foster parents Mr and Mrs Williams who have two children, Ben and Amalia. This scenario occurred one month before video scene 4.

Activity 6   **Video scene 5 'The visit'**

Allow 20–30 minutes

Play scene 5. First of all just watch and take in what is happening. Then rewind the tape and watch the sequence again. This time listen carefully to what is being said and make some notes on:

(a)   the way the visit has been organised and how well informed the different parties are about each other

Lloyd, Maggie and the Williamses

(b)   Maggie's competence in supporting Lloyd during the visit and enabling him to be himself. To help you with this consider the following skills and, alongside each, make a note of how competent you think Maggie is at each one:

listening

being supportive

facilitating/enabling.

Comment   (a)   It appears from the way Mrs Williams greets Maggie that this meeting has been organised in advance and that they are expected. From the interaction between Lloyd and Mr Williams it is obvious that they have been told quite a lot about Lloyd, the things he likes to do, his school and where his mother lives. Lloyd is pretty shy and doesn't say very much, but that seems fairly typical for a 13-year-old in a strange situation.

Maggie keeps quite a low profile in this visit. However, she does help Lloyd overcome his initial shyness by drawing attention to the football magazine on the table. This provides an initial focus for conversation with Mr Williams. It is something Lloyd, Mr Williams and his son Ben all have in common.

Maggie also enables Lloyd to say a little about himself and his own family. She does not speak for him, rather she prompts him into speaking on his own behalf, saying 'you go over to see your mum and your sister, don't you, often'. She also helps the conversation to flow by adding in little bits of information like the diving.

(b)   So how did you assess Maggie's competence in this situation. I thought that she contributed to what was a fairly positive experience in the following ways:

Skills	Competence
Listening	fairly good, does not talk a great deal but seems to be actively listening – you can tell by her face
Being supportive	again good, she draws attention to things she knows Lloyd will be interested in, e.g. the football magazine. She doesn't talk down to him. You sense that she knows he is feeling a bit uncomfortable
Facilitating/ enabling	good, she offers information but doesn't tell the whole story for Lloyd – leaves him to give information about himself

To summarise then, the positive experiences observed here include:

- the meeting is planned and is not rushed
- all parties obviously have some information about each other
- the atmosphere is friendly if not exactly relaxed; the foster carers are very welcoming
- the young person is not talked down to
- the parties ask questions of each other, people begin to get to know each other, some common ground is established
- there is a recognition that not everything may go smoothly
- the young person has time to look around, familiarise himself
- the worker does not intervene too much or speak on behalf of the young person.

Section 2
Planning life in a care setting

We are now going to look at one of the most important aspects of managing transitions: the area of care planning. Care planning has been mentioned before in Block 2 and to help with this work we are going to start by looking back at two of the earlier case studies. First Mr Bright and work at the Redwood Day Unit and second, care planning at Liberty of Earley House.

If you think back to the Redwood Day Unit where Mr Bright spends his days, you will remember how Brenda Masters and Ceinwen Conroy talked about their work and the skills they have developed for caring for people who have dementia. (You might like to look back to Activity 15, Unit 7 and the Media Notes at this point.) They also outlined how people are referred to the day unit and how they 'get to know them'.

Activity 7

Allow about 10 minutes

Getting to know you

Read through this short quote from Ceinwen. Note the main ways they 'get to know people' at Redwood and the skills that are used here. When reading this it is useful to remember that Ceinwen and Brenda are both senior care workers at the day unit but also keyworkers for particular people.

> *We tend to get referrals and as they go through from the manager we receive them and then they are passed on to the keyworkers and we take a bit of background history from the referral – there is always a little bit of background history. From there, if possible, we will go out and meet with the carer or we will invite the carer and the client in and we will discuss likes and dislikes, past life, what their abilities have been, the kind of lifestyle they have had and then generally get to know a bit of their background and observe them on the first few days here and get to know a bit about their character. Be very aware of things that they were once skilful in and can now no longer manage.*

Comment

Ceinwen mentions the following ways of 'getting to know people':

- referrals are received from the manager – some written information may be passed on here

- being a keyworker

- workers visiting people in their own homes before they make a move

- getting to know about a person's past life, some background history is passed on from family, some from other professionals

- getting to know people, their likes and dislikes, what they can and cannot do for themselves

- observing people during their first few days within a new setting

- awareness of ability.

We can see that the skills involved here include those of:

- listening
- discussing
- observing
- being aware
- recording.

They are communication skills which we will be looking at in more detail in Unit 17.

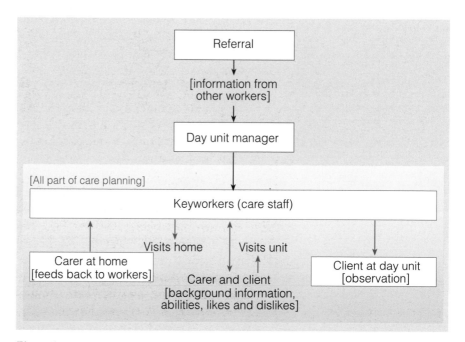

Figure 1

To help you understand the process I have set it out as a diagram (Figure 1). You can see that what is happening is a two-way process between the day unit staff and the client and informal carer at home. If you look back to Unit 7, you will remember that carers are encouraged to contact the unit about things that are happening at home and I have included this feedback on the diagram. The process of care planning may begin with a referral which is fed down to the keyworkers but the real work is about piecing together information about the individual, negotiating plans, and monitoring a changing situation. Where the person cannot communicate well then observing behaviour becomes very important.

The nature of the work described here is all part of planning the care that people receive while living or spending time in a care environment. There will be a written *care plan* for Mr Bright and care plans are found in a range of settings – hospitals, day units, domestic homes, residential homes – wherever there is a need to record the support a person needs and the care to be provided.

If you look back at the work you did in Unit 8 (Activity 3) you will remember that negotiating a care plan was a key part of the way staff worked with residents at Liberty of Earley House. There the care plan formed a record or a guide to enabling residents to do things for themselves within their own abilities. Marion Whitehead said:

> *It's important that we don't take over the resident's life for them, that we find out how much they can do for themselves and encourage them to do as much as possible. Provided that the resident isn't getting upset it doesn't matter how long a task takes, it's just so important that they do things for themselves as much as they can.*

This is an important reason for care planning. It is a way of establishing people's needs and giving them choices over how they are met. Staff should only give support if needed. Ann Hamilton said:

> *It's very difficult to strike that balance because a lot of staff find it easier to go in and do everything because it's quicker and it's important that they understand the reasons behind being enablers.*

The care plan is really a tool to help the worker to get to know the resident. It's a way of helping people to maintain their self-identity in situations where they are in danger of becoming 'just another old person' or 'just another child in care'.

In order to become familiar with another person's needs you need time and you need to talk about a lot of things. When Marion talked on Audio Cassette 2 about the scope of the care plan at Liberty of Earley House she mentioned: medical needs, daily routines, things people like to do for themselves, anything they might need assistance with, food and special diets, social life, money matters. These kinds of issues are recorded on a form and to be a useful record they have to be revised, updated and communicated to others. Again Marion said:

> *It's reviewed after six weeks and then at six monthly intervals, but as a resident's needs change so it's renewed – if somebody were taken ill or their general health changed or if they needed a different form of care then it would be updated.*

We will look at a section of the Liberty of Earley Care Plan in a moment, but first we are going to look at a part of the process of care planning which involves *negotiating*. Again, we are going to use the skills video, only this time moving away from child care to focus on an older person who has recently moved into a residential home. This scenario shows part of a conversation which forms the basis of care planning around managing medication. The older person, Dora, who has epilepsy, is talking to Jean, her keyworker.

Jean is trying to complete a section of the care plan concerned with whether or not Dora needs help taking her medication. They also talk about how Dora's health should be monitored.

Activity 8   **Video scene 6 'Getting to know you'**

Allow 20–30 minutes

Play scene 6. Now rewind the tape and play it again. This time make some notes about the following.

(a)   Do you think that this aspect of the care plan is negotiated? If so, why?

(b) Write down at least two ways in which Dora plays an active part in this discussion over how her medication will be managed and how staff should monitor her actions.

(c) What skills does Jean demonstrate in this exchange?

(d) Could this practice be improved?

Jean and Dora

Comment (a) I thought it did seem negotiated as both sides put forward their views and a decision was reached. Jean made the offer that the care staff could be responsible for Dora's tablets, bringing them 'with the morning tea' and at 'supper'. She also says that staff could 'pop in ... and check that everything's alright during the night'. Dora rejects both of these offers of support and talks about the way she has managed in the past and intends to manage in the future even though she acknowledges that she may need help if she has an attack.

(b) Dora plays an active part in this discussion by:
- talking about her illness and the medication
- accepting the responsibility for taking her medication as well as the risk that may be involved if she has an attack
- acknowledging that she welcomes support when she has an attack. She says, 'Penny came along and made me a cup of tea and generally helped me. I was grateful for that.'

(c) Some of the skills Jean demonstrates are:
- active listening
- enabling Dora to talk about herself
- assessing the situation and recording a decision
- giving information about the kind of support staff can give.

(d) At first, Jean appears a little nervous about talking to Dora about the care plan. She doesn't really remind her what it is about, 'It's that form we were filling in'. Reminding Dora of the process of care planning may have been a good idea. For example, where is this form kept and who sees it?

She also appears ready to assume that Dora will forget to take her medication and that it might be better for staff to give it to her. Fortunately Dora, who is quite in control of her medicine, gently puts her in her place. But this does not always happen, often there is an assumption that because someone is old, they are bound to forget things. It is all too easy for kind concern to become ageist practice in these situations.

Care plans can cover a wide range of topics, after all they need to consider all aspects of everyday living. But while the conversations between residents and staff, like Dora and Jean, can take time as they cover the details of personal history, recording that information in a form that means something to other people is another matter. You'll be looking at records in more detail in Block 5. Here we consider how the information from the type of interview you have just observed gets translated onto paper.

Activity 9   Information on a form

Allow about 10 minutes   Here is the section of the care plan used at Liberty of Earley House which is concerned with medication. I have filled it in as if I were Jean having just talked to Dora. If you were another care assistant reading this part of the form, what would it tell you? What would Jean know about Dora and her medication that you could not know by reading the form?

18	MEDICATION	DATE	19.5.97				
a	Takes no medication at present						
b	Takes full charge of own medication		✓				
c	Can take charge of weeks supply						
d	Can take charge of days supply						
e	Cannot be responsible for any medication						
	COMMENTS	Happy to continue with own routine for taking medication for epilepsy. If has an attack welcomes support but wishes to manage as far as possible. (19.5.97)					

Comment   As a care assistant reading this form, I would know that Dora takes full charge of her own medication, that she has epilepsy and may need some assistance if she has an attack. I would not know what Dora's medication consists of, or that she takes other tablets apart from those for the epilepsy. I wouldn't know how long she has had these conditions; how she has managed them during her life or the routines she had developed. I wouldn't know that she feels strongly about managing on her own, while acknowledging that she might sometimes need help.

As you will see later on in the course, recording information is an important skill which can be helped or hindered by the forms and schedules used. In this case, the 'comments' box is very small so there is not much room to record information. Changes of shifts and handovers between staff can be important times for passing on information about people on a daily basis, whereas the care plan is a more formal written record. Both are part of care planning.

Section 3
Principles of practice

By now you will recognise that alongside practical skills and underlying knowledge, the principles and values held by care workers and care organisations have an important part to play in developing care relationships. To complete this unit on practice skills, we ask you to reflect on the first of the principles of good practice outlined in Unit 5: 'enable people to develop their own potential'.

Activity 10	'Enable people to develop their own potential'
Allow about 10 minutes	Look back through the activities in this unit and, using all the evidence you have accumulated from these activities, complete the chart below. Try to give at least two examples of the ways in which the principle of 'enabling people to develop their own potential' has been promoted or has failed to be upheld.

	Promoted	Failed to promote
Enable people to develop their own potential	• Lloyd's new foster family welcomed him and encouraged his sporty activities - boosting his self confidence and feeling of acceptance, and told him his friends were welcome to visit. • Freda in Unit 8 was encouraged to warn herself and take responsibility for what she could reasonably accomplish. • Tracey, Joan's keyworker enabled her to do her own shopping and leave the home for visits out. • Mother - injured right hand - dislocated thumb and severed fingers - physiotherapist taught her exercises to do at home to strengthen. Enabled her to have some control over disability and care and recovery.	• Lloyd's keyworker did not ask Lloyd's opinions re: move, nor was available to assist - Appeared relieved and did not consider that he would not be able to say goodbye to friend. • Jenny is frustrated by her inability to visit the garden, and as staff and resources are not organised to try to facilitate this. • Mother - injured hand (see opposite), not consulted re injuries - misdiagnosed - treatment nor medication, felt unable to ask questions. Not made aware of options by Doctor. Loss of control and self-confidence. • Aunt - diagnosed - terminal cancer in hospital - moved directly to residential care setting nor able to say goodbye to home or pets.

• Friend - tested for epilepsy - procedures explained fully by nurse. Options + opinions discussed fully ... aware of results and understood.

Displacement - no counselling offered.

Comment   Here are some of the examples that we came up with:

	Promoted	**Failed to promote**
Enable people to develop their own potential	• The way Lloyd was encouraged to talk about things he likes doing when meeting his new foster family. • Ceinwen talking about 'getting to know' the older people at the day unit and understanding their abilities.	• The way Esther was trapped in a hospital environment because there wasn't the right kind of accommodation available. • Fran's poor handling of the planning for Lloyd's move to foster care, which could have undermined his confidence.

In this final activity on practice you can see that while the contexts of care can vary between settings in terms of the physical, social or organisational environments, common issues can emerge for people on the receiving end of care. For people moving between settings and 'living in care' the importance of offering support during transitions and of enabling people to maintain control over their lives is crucial to the maintenance of well-being.

Make sure you store the work you have done on Unit 9 activities so far in your K100 portfolio. You can use them as evidence of your achievements.

Section 4
Staying on top

A theme running through the study skills boxes in Block 2 has been the importance of keeping up your morale. In Unit 6 I talked about not letting the number work get you down. In Unit 7 I discussed the value of being able to find yourself a place to study away from the distractions of daily life – a personal space where you can think your own thoughts and develop your mind. But I also acknowledged how easy it is to drop out of a distance learning course, and the importance of talking to other people when your spirits are low, to get things back in perspective. I recognised the ever-present challenge of the sheer quantity of work, but also that very few people manage to complete every last thing. Similarly in Unit 8 I talked about the importance of keeping things in proportion – not taking too many notes and thereby turning the course into a dreary chore. This theme is pulled together under the general idea of keeping yourself on top of the course.

Study skills: 'Riding' the course (not letting it ride you)

This is *your* course. You have paid for it and it's your time you are giving up. It's up to you to make of it what you can in the time you have available. How much of the course you can get through will depend partly on what

- *knowledge* and *skill* you bring with you.

It will also depend on your

- *circumstances* – how much time you can set aside for study, how often you are interrupted and so on.

And some people just study faster than others.

As long as you feel you are learning and making valuable progress you just have to do the best you can. Nobody else will know what you do and don't do. You simply submit your assignments and the rest is your own business.

Approach the course strategically. From time to time, think to yourself 'Why am I doing K100? What do I want to get out of it? How does it weigh in the balance against other things in my life?' Then make your own choices as you go along. Specialise in those parts of the course that interest you most. Cut corners when you are short of time. Leave out sections of units if you are falling behind. And most of all *make sure you are enjoying the course*, not letting it become a chore. In *any* course there tends to be much more to read than will fit into the time available. Don't get depressed. Being a successful student means taking control – making your own choices about what to complete and what to leave out – not letting the course get the upper hand, but making it take you where you want to go.

4.1 Working with numbers

The number-work exercise below builds on the table reading skills you developed in Unit 6 and your reading of *The Good Study Guide*.

> **Study skills: Reviewing numbers skills**
>
> You have already read Chapter 4 of *The Good Study Guide*. However, you will find it useful to consolidate what you learnt – the insights and tips – by looking back through it now. Just spend about 15 minutes reminding yourself of what it says.

Planning services for older people

Table 1 could be very useful to you in planning services for older people in your area. Imagine you are setting up a meals-on-wheels service and you are wondering what age groups to target it at. You have been involved in a lunch club and you have the impression that the people attending it are spread fairly evenly right across the age range from retirement onwards. But how reliable is this impression and will the pattern of demand be the same for meals-on-wheels?

If you were to visit a library and look at the government publication *Social Trends* for 1997, you would see that it has just the information you need.

Table 1   Use of selected personal social services by age, 1994–95 (United Kingdom)

Percentages

	65–69	70–74	75–79	80–84	85 and over	All aged 65 and over
Meals-on-wheels	3	17	11	28	40	100
Local authority home help	9	15	20	25	30	100
District nurse/health visitor	10	17	19	27	28	100
Voluntary organisation	8	15	27	27	23	100
Private home help	14	20	25	20	20	100
Lunch club	16	17	19	30	19	100
Day centre	16	24	21	26	13	100

(Source: Office for National Statistics, 1997)

As with any table you need to take a little time to find your way around these numbers.

Activity 11
Allow about 5 minutes

(a) What do the numbers 65–69 and so on at the tops of the columns mean?

(b) What does the number 3 at the top of the first column of figures mean? Try writing a sentence saying what it means.

Comment   (a)   I hope this one was fairly obvious. 65–69 is the lowest age group in the table. The highest is 85 years and over.

(b)   The 3 isn't so obvious though. You can see it stands next to 'meals-on-wheels' – and at the top right of the table you can see 'percentages'. So the 3 means 3 per cent and it's to do with meals-on-wheels. But 3 per cent of what? Does it mean that 3 per cent of 65–69 year-olds use meals-on-wheels? Or does it mean that 3 per cent of the people using meals-on-wheels are between 65 and 69? How can you tell?

The last column gives us a clue. It says that all the age groups added together make 100 per cent. You can try quickly adding together the numbers in the top row. They come to 99, which is near enough to 100 (some of the numbers must have been rounded down).

This tells us that the 3 means 3 per cent of all age groups. In other words, out of all the users of meals-on-wheels, 3 per cent are aged 65–69.

Activity 12   (a)   What percentage of meals-on-wheels users are over 85 years old?

Allow about 10 minutes   (b)   What percentage of meals-on-wheels users are over 80 years old?

(c)   What proportion of meals-on-wheels users are under 75?

(d)   Is the impression that lunch club attenders are fairly evenly spread across the age bands correct?

(e)   Are the majority of lunch club attenders over 80 years old?

(f)   Which age group is the biggest user of private home help?

(g)   Which age group makes the most demand on day centres?

(h)   When were these data gathered?

Comment   (a)   40 per cent of meals-on-wheels users are over 85. If you didn't get this answer go back to the explanation of the 3 per cent.

(b)   This is slightly tricky. If you answered 28 per cent, you forgot that the 85+ group are also over 80. To answer Question (b) you need to add the 28 per cent to the 40 per cent for the older group. This gives 68 per cent of meals-on-wheels users being over 80 years old, in other words just over two-thirds.

(c)   To find the number of meals-on-wheels users under 75, you need to add the 65–69 group to the 70–75 group (3 + 17 = 20). So if your area is similar to the national picture, you should expect 20 per cent of users of the service to be under 75. (Another way to say this is 1 in 5.)

(d)   The biggest group of lunch club attenders is the 80–85s who make up 30 per cent. However, the size of each of the other groups is between 16 and 19 per cent. So, apart from that 'bulge' in the lower 80s, the ages of attenders are pretty evenly spread.

(e)   To get this answer, you need once again to add the 80–85 group to the 85 and over group (30 + 19 = 49). This is very nearly 50 per cent, or half. So the answer is no.

(f)   Scanning along the row for 'private home help', you can see that the biggest figure is 25 per cent for the 75–79 age group. So that is the answer. However, the figures for the other over 70 age groups are not far behind at 20 per cent.

(g) The 80–84 group makes the most demand on day centres, at 26 per cent. However the 70–74 group is very close behind at 24 per cent. Rather oddly, the 75–79 group is slightly lower at 21 per cent. Can you think of possible reasons for lower use by this group? Either this is a puzzle to work out, or we just assume that it is the random variation which always tends to push figures up or down a few percentage points. To go back to the question, basically each group in the 70 to 85 year band makes a substantial demand on day centres, while the under 70s and over 85s attend in rather lower numbers.

(h) Although published in 1997, the data were actually gathered in 1994–5. The box on p. 96 of *The Good Study Guide* discusses this.

Now you have done the activities in this unit you are well prepared for Part 3 of TMA 02. It is based on Table 1 and asks very similar questions to the ones you have just answered. If you have any doubts as you work on the assignment, go back to the explanations above.

4.2 Developing your writing skills

Study skills: Treating essay writing as a craft

Finally, before you start work on your TMA for Block 2, it is a good time to read some more about essay writing in *The Good Study Guide*. In Unit 5 you read part of Chapter 5 which explored essay writing by looking at some samples. We will return to that chapter in the next block, but you also need to be thinking about the writing process itself, so that you can plan your approach to your assignments. As Chapter 6 explains, putting together an assignment involves a lot more than just sitting down at your desk and letting the words flow. Read Sections 1–3 of Chapter 6 now.

End of block assignment

Now you have finished your reading for Block 2, it is time to write your assignment: TMA 02. You will find details in the Assignment Book.

Study skills: Study diary

When you have finished TMA 02, it will be a good point at which to bring your study diary up to date. And now that you are about a third of the way through the course, it would also be a good idea to go back over your diary for the first two blocks to review your progress. Instead of just reflecting back over the last week or so, look back over the whole nine weeks. What has been going well? What has not been so good? Do you need to make any adjustments in your study approach? Do you feel you have made important strides since you started? Comparing your first diary notes with your most recent ones should make interesting reading.

Reference

Office for National Statistics (1997) *Social Trends 27*, 1997 Edition, HMSO, London.

Acknowledgements

Grateful acknowledgement is made to the following source for permission to reproduce material in this unit:

Table 1: Office for National Statistics (1997) *Social Trends 27*, 1997 Edition. Reproduced by permission of the Office for National Statistics, © Crown Copyright.

Grateful acknowledgement is also made to the following sources for permission to reproduce the illustrations on the front cover of this block: all Sally and Richard Greenhill except *top right* Brenda Prince/Format and *bottom right* John Birdsall Photography.